IT'S A LITTLE INCONVENIENT

Memories of a Bulawayo Book Club

Althea Farren

ORIGINAL WRITING

ISBNS
PARENT : 978-1-909007-49-9
EPUB: 978-1-909007-75-8
MOBI: 978-1-909007-76-5

A CIP catalogue for this book is available from the National Library.

Published by ORIGINAL WRITING LTD., Dublin, 2012.

Printed by CLONDALKIN GROUP, Glasnevin, Dublin 11

ACKNOWLEDGEMENTS:

My sincere thanks to all the people who have made a contribution to this book:

To Larry for his love, support, patience and encouragement.

To Glyn, Sean, Brian and Carl.

To Mike Dicey for designing the cover.

To my editor, Isobel Creed.

To those friends who have given me advice and encouragement.

To the Book Club ladies, past and present.

Contents

"The law of the land must also work for moral justice - if I lead the people on the land and then get time to bring about law and order then it is a far better proposition, a better approach than one which will pit the forces against the masses of people now occupying the land and there would be greater death, greater bloodshed - this is just a little row of trespass."

"Elsewhere, those who commit murders are being arrested, those who commit robberies are being arrested, other crimes are being taken care of and there is greater law and order.

*Only in the little area of trespass on the farms, where there has in fact been injustice all along by the farmers and if they suffer this very little - shall I say - inconvenience of their land being occupied. And **they suffer that very little inconvenience**, against the inconvenience that we have suffered as a people for decades."*

ROBERT GABRIEL MUGABE

BBC interview with David Dimbleby – 26 June 2000

Prologue: Memories

"The wind was a torrent of darkness among the gusty trees,
The moon was a ghostly galleon tossed upon cloudy seas,
The road was a ribbon of moonlight over the purple moor,
And the highwayman came riding, riding, riding,
The highwayman came riding
Up to the old inn-door..."

A horseman gallops urgently through the wind-raked moonlit night towards an assignation with the woman he loves. As he draws closer, we see that he is wearing "a coat of claret velvet", a white, lacy shirt, soft doeskin breeches and long, thigh-high boots. We hear the clatter of his horse's hooves on the cobblestones and we tingle with excitement as we listen to his whistled tune. The beautiful Bess loosens her long, black hair. It cascades down upon his upturned face in waves of sweet, intoxicating perfume.

But in the darkness, out of sight of the lovers, the envious villain lurks. He informs the redcoat troops of the highwayman's relationship with the innkeeper's daughter. They set a trap for him. Bravely refusing to keep silent and allow him to be captured, loyal Bess warns her lover - by shooting herself. The highwayman discovers that she has given her life for him. Crazed with grief, he rides recklessly back to the inn. As he comes within range, the soldiers shoot him down like a dog.

We wipe our eyes, as we picture his broken body lying in the road, the red blood seeping through his claret jacket and staining the flawless white lace of his shirt. Perhaps it is better to die, though, than to live without the person you love.

We gaze up at our mother sitting in her enchanted circle of golden light. She lowers the worn poetry book for a moment to smile at our enraptured expressions.

"What happens next?" asks Glyn. "Is that the end?"

"No," says our mother gently. "Not quite."

Her voice becomes even more thrilling. She whispers so faintly that we have to lean forward to catch her words:

"And still on a winter's night, they say, when the wind is in the trees,
When the moon is a ghostly galleon tossed upon cloudy seas,
When the road is a ribbon of moonlight over the purple moor,
A highwayman comes riding, riding, riding
A highwayman comes riding up to the old inn-door..."

Once again, his horse's hooves break the silence. Once more, at his signal, Bess opens her bedroom window. And once more, she leans out, towards him, plaiting the dark red love knot into her long black hair...

We shiver with satisfaction. The ghostly lovers have been reunited forever, far from the loathsome ostler, Tim, and far beyond the muskets of King George's men....

"Bed-time, darlings," mum says, blowing out our candles.

Sleep eludes us. We open the bedroom curtains so that we can look out at the stars and whisper secrets to each other.

Would a highwayman ever ride down our farm road?

Was Pookie 'who put the world right' the only rabbit with wings?

Could fairies fly as far as the stars?

Was that the wishing chair up there, near the moon, moving across the sky?

Long ago, three young children on a remote farm knew all about the magic of books.

Part I

The Book Club: Early Days

1976 - 1983

The Book Club

It was Veronica's suggestion that we start a Book Club.

There would be twelve of us. We'd meet on the first Saturday morning of every month. Each person would review the books she had read. We would contribute an agreed amount of money so that the two people whose turn it was could buy books. The hostess for the month would provide tea for the group.

"It's time we stopped talking about teething problems and the best way to potty train our children," said Veronica. "My brain is a mush of fruit puree and jelly these days. We'll make it a rule not to utter one word about nappies or how to discipline children."

When I left home in Marandellas to go to university in Pietermaritzburg, South Africa at the age of seventeen, I believed that, at some point during the three year Bachelor of Arts course, I'd come to know what career path to take.

I wasn't going to be a teacher. That was the one thing I did know. My mother was a teacher. I wanted to be something different. Something much more glamorous.

I muddled through to graduation without the expected epiphany.

I found my first two jobs (in a bank and in the accounts department of a large retailer) soul-destroying. This was hardly surprising, since I hated working with figures and had been useless at maths at school.

I didn't last very long in the accounting job. I couldn't count money accurately. And I was far too slow. I finally messed up big time when I was told to prepare the company's cheques for the month. The term "(Pty.) Limited" related to South African companies. My cheques were nice and neat, but the correct abbreviation for Rhodesian companies was "(Pvt.) Limited". The whole lot had to be cancelled. Someone else was given the job of re-writing them.

"Why aren't you teaching?" the manager asked. "You've got a degree, haven't you?"

He had a daughter at St. Peter's – a private school in Bulawayo. He was also chairman of the Board of Governors. In spite of the cheque fiasco (or, perhaps, because of it), he recommended me to the headmistress, and, within a few weeks, I was teaching English and Biblical Studies and loving every moment.

Larry and I met in 1969 and married the following year. He'd come out to Africa from Ireland several years before, to join the British South Africa Police. Our first son, Sean, was born in 1972 and Brian, our second son, in 1974.

Every Friday we brought our babies to be weighed at the Princess Margaret Rose Clinic. Each week, we would describe the consistency of their stools, and recount our heroic efforts to avoid demand feeding. Seventies babies were to be fed only at regular, prescribed intervals. If we allowed ourselves to fall into the insidious trap of demand feeding, our babies would become undisciplined tyrants when they were older. We new mothers, on no account, were to allow ourselves to be manipulated. We had to remain firm, resolute and responsible. Sticking to a rigid routine was the ONLY way to bring up children. Dr. Spock had "a lot to answer for".

When the babies had been checked (and reprimands or compliments dispensed), we'd converge on Meikles for waffles and coffee in a profusion of prams and pushchairs.

Shortly after Brian was born, I started studying for a Higher Education Diploma through UNISA, South Africa's correspondence university in Pretoria. I became adept at making notes for Pedagogics assignments in the dining room, whilst simultaneously gauging exactly how far Sean was from my stunted delicious monster plant in the lounge. I developed such acute hearing, that I could shout "No" as he was raising his hand to tear off another leaf.

The first book club meeting was held at Veronica's lovely house in Hillside. Our hostess, married to a prominent businessman in the city, was a little older than the rest of us, and certainly more confident and mature. With severely-cut short, straight dark hair, thick glasses and a brusque but kindly manner, she was the epitome of an intellectual.

Twelve chairs had been arranged in a circle in her lounge. We'd been asked to bring four of our favourite books, one of which we'd review and then all four would be put into the "library".

The children were in the garden, far away from the locked swimming pool, in the care of two black maids: Florence and Happiness, who were smartly turned out for the occasion in crisp aprons and neat caps. Florence, my maid, was looking unimpressed, as usual, even though she'd been quite pleased with her new uniform. Happiness, Lisa's domestic, was always cheerful and good-natured. She loved children, unlike Florence, who would rather have been at home ironing.

There was a toy fire engine, a tipper truck, racing cars, a large dolls' house and an assortment of balls to play with. Under the trees, a picnic had been laid out. My boys were delighted to find their favourite "animal" biscuits with iced pictures of elephants, hippos and giraffes that you licked off; little cakes decorated with hundreds and thousands and ice cream. Veronica had also provided a jug of home-made lemonade and a couple of large bottles of caterpillar-green cream soda.

"It's a birthday party, mum," said Sean.

"Thank you for coming, everyone," said Veronica. "We have a number of objectives. First and foremost, I believe that a book club should be fun. We must *enjoy* our monthly meetings. Even the most devoted mother needs to get away from her kids from time to time. It must also be intellectually stimulating. We all love reading, otherwise we wouldn't be here. We'll benefit from one another's ideas and tastes and we'll accumulate books that we might not have heard of before, let alone read."

"I'll start the ball rolling. I suggest that, in future, we write out our reviews before each meeting, and put the comments into the books we've discussed. Remarks can be added, too, by subsequent readers."

Veronica's first choice was 'Nineteen Eighty-Four'.

"The author was born in 1903," she began. "Shortly before his death in 1950, an admirer wrote: *'You have made an indelible mark on English literature... you are among the few memorable writers of your generation.'* George Orwell was particularly concerned about unjust social systems and about the rising power of fascism.

In 'Nineteen Eighty-Four' he writes of a miserable world, devoid of comfort, individuality and spontaneity.

The Thought Police are an ever-present threat. No one is allowed even to think of criticising the system and everyone has to conform to party requirements. Children are encouraged to spy on their parents. Marriage is for the purpose of procreation only. The expression of love and sexual pleasure are feelings that are actively discouraged."

"Old-fashioned science fiction," hissed Rachel on my right. "Give me Sidney Sheldon any day! There's no way I'm going to *enjoy* George Orwell."

"Winston meets Julia," Veronica continued, ignoring Rachel. "She's not as intelligent as he is, but she is rashly rebellious. They take risks to spend time together. Inevitably they are caught, tortured and forced to betray one another."

"'Nineteen Eighty-Four'," concluded Veronica, "is a about the evil of a totalitarian regime that brainwashes its people in a cynical and amoral manner. We are living in the year 1976 in Rhodesia. What will our country be like in 1984? Will the world be any different?"

Many of us had heard of "Nineteen Eighty-Four", but only Veronica had actually read it. And she had an honours degree in maths, not in English literature.

"Goodness, Veronica," said Lisa laughing. (There had been a respectful silence for a moment.) "How do you expect us to give our mundane reviews after such a learned commentary? Some of us are just ordinary housewives."

Veronica smiled. "I enjoyed working on my presentation. I don't expect all of you to spend time on preparation if you don't want to. Basically, we'd like to know whether you enjoyed what you've read and why."

"Do you think things *will* be different eight years from now?" asked Pam. She had long dark hair pulled back in a pony tail and a gentle rather diffident way of speaking. "Perhaps the war will be over. It can't go on much longer, surely? In 1984 Sandy will be in high school."

"We might be facing majority rule by then," said Veronica. There was a chorus of dissent.

"Not going to happen," said Rachel glaring at Veronica. "Not a chance. Smithy's not going to hand the country over to the blacks. 'Never in a thousand years' he's said.[1] In 1984 we'll be talking about books and having tea just like we are today."

"An alpha female," I thought. "*And* a true believer."

"OK, Pam, you have the floor," said Veronica, settling back in her chair. She didn't seem at all perturbed

"My favourite author," began Pam, "is Wilbur Smith. I thought his first novel 'When the Lion Feeds' was brilliant. The sequel 'The Sound of Thunder', which continues the saga of the Courtneys, was just as exciting. I've been given his new book 'Shout at the Devil'. I haven't started it yet, but I believe it's excellent, and I'd like to put it into Book Club. I'm just going to read the 'blurb' on the back cover. Whoever chooses it can comment on it next month."

"'*From jaunty start to grim finale*, Shout at the Devil *moves with all the ebullience and power of the brilliant, incorrigible, gin-drinking old brigand that is its central character.*

Hilarious comedy gives way to spine-chilling horror at the climax of the novel, as Flynn, Sebastian and Rosa come to learn that death and violence are no longer a grotesque joke – but a savage reality.

With action on every page, battle, murder and sudden death, Shout at the Devil *is not for quiet evening enjoyment by peace-loving readers. It is for the adventure-lovers and thrill-seekers.*'"

---

1 Ian Douglas Smith was Prime Minister of Rhodesia for 15 years. He said that black majority rule would never happen in Rhodesia. "Never in a thousand years..."

"I'm sure you're all Wilbur Smith fans," said Pam, holding the book up to show us the cover.

I sneaked a look at Veronica. Her face was expressionless.

Margaret was next. I didn't know her very well. She taught at Townsend, Bulawayo's most prestigious girls' school. I found her rather distant. Perhaps she was reserved. Like Veronica, she had come out to Africa from England several years before.

"The most wonderful romance of all time, in my opinion, is Jane Austen's 'Pride and Prejudice'," she said. "It's a book that I read over and over again and never tire of. It's still extremely popular because it raises issues with which we can all empathise. We cringe at Mrs Bennet's crass, vulgar behaviour and sympathise with sensible, sensitive Elizabeth and Jane, who have to put up with their silly, trivial younger sisters. Darcy is every girl's dream, even though he comes over, at first, as very much aware of his own superiority and importance. It's difficult to blame him. Mrs Bennet is such an embarrassment with her obsessive dedication to husband hunting.

Mr Collins is repulsive and Lady Catherine equally so, but the experience is good for Elizabeth, who is able to put them both in their place. She sees Wickham for what he is after he elopes with Lydia, and learns the hard way that appearances can be misleading. When the more mature Elizabeth, in the company of sensible relations, meets Darcy again, she comes to understand and appreciate the true character of the man who loves her. Her reaction to his second proposal of marriage is very different."

Those who had read 'Pride and Prejudice' began to talk animatedly.

"Darcy is such a gorgeous man. No wonder Elizabeth finds him irresistible…"

"I'd have his shoes under my bed any time…"

"Imagine coping with a mother-in-law like that. Mine's bad enough, but Mrs Bennet is one hell of a lot worse…"

Margaret obviously loved the classics and seemed delighted at the positive response.

"We'd better move on," said Veronica. "Your turn, Althea."

"I love Rumer Godden's style," I began tentatively. "I've read 'The Greengage Summer', 'Kingfishers Catch Fire' and 'The Battle of the Villa Fiorita'. 'In This House of Brede' is the book I'm going to talk about."

I'd decided to write down what I wanted to say, so that I could read my review if I felt nervous.

"Talented, highly-regarded Mrs Philippa Talbot leaves her important job in the Civil Service to become a Benedictine nun. Philippa explains to her young colleague Penny that 'an enclosed order is like a power house of prayer...' 'The walls,' she says 'are not to enclose the power, but to stop unauthorised people getting in to hinder its working...' The nuns are ordinary human beings, with weaknesses and strengths like everyone else.

Some people might consider women in an 'enclosed' convent to be peculiar religious fanatics, eccentrics who choose a cloistered way of life to escape the world. Theirs is a strange peace, 'made of unremitting toil and effort...yet peace all the same...' I felt profoundly satisfied at the outcome of Philippa's journey."

There was a slightly embarrassed silence.

My friend Nina, also a Catholic, said supportively, "Well, that's certainly a book I shall read."

Beside me, Rachel gave an audible snort. "I sincerely hope that we won't be discussing religion and politics all the time."

"Your turn, Rachel," I said.

What a cow. Who'd invited her to join us?

She'd brought 'The Eiger Sanction' by Trevanian, a new author none of us had heard of. Unfortunately, it sounded intriguing.

"The hero, Jonathan Hemlock, carries out 'sanctions' or assassinations to finance his collection of paintings. He is tricked into undertaking a dangerous assignment, which entails climbing the deadly North Face of the Eiger Mountain. The reader's interest is guaranteed as early as page 3, where Trevanian describes a secret agent's skull being crushed. 'The pain was very sharp indeed, but the sound was more terrible. It was akin to biting into crisp celery with your hands over your ears – but more intimate.'"

"Gross!" said Nina, shuddering.

"Disgusting," Veronica agreed.

Everyone else laughed. It was obvious that "The Eiger Sanction" was going to be a popular choice.

We numbered our books and entered the information in a journal Veronica had bought. The hostess would choose first each month, and then everyone else would follow in rotation. We each contributed $5 towards the purchase of new books.

Veronica's tea was delicious. She was one of those people who did everything well. The conversation swung from books to social events, and to the question of when it was likely to rain. The water level in our dams was always a concern, especially in the hot, dry months of September and October.

Afterwards, Florence and I collected the blanket, spare nappies, bottles and dummies and loaded the boys into the car. Florence took the fire engine away from Sean and he gave a couple of token howls. Brian was already asleep.

Book Club *was* going to be fun.

WAR YEARS

These were the days of call-ups. All men of our husbands' age had to do national service duties either in the Territorial Army, the Police or Internal Affairs. While a member of the regular police, Larry had been in PATU, the Police Anti-terrorist Unit. After leaving the police, he joined SWAT (Special Weapons and Tactics).

Unfortunately, Sean and Brian didn't get to see their father rappelling like Spiderman from the fire department tower or abseiling down steep granite rock-faces in the Matopos Hills. For them, PATU and SWAT duty meant Saturday and Sunday afternoons at the police camp swimming pool. When Larry was on call-up, we were allowed to visit him, if his stick[2] hadn't been called out, but he couldn't come home.

Both wings of the black independence movement, ZANU (Shona) and ZAPU (Ndebele) had been embroiled in an armed struggle against the white-dominated government of Rhodesia since the 1960s. The conflict had intensified after Mozambique had been handed over to FRELIMO by the Portuguese government in 1975. ZIPRA (ZAPU's military wing) and ZANLA (ZANU's military wing) waged their guerrilla war from their bases in sympathetic and supportive Zambia and Mozambique, and had succeeded in infiltrating a large proportion of rural Rhodesia. They had passed the stage of launching furtive, isolated in-and-out raids, and had established themselves as a resolute presence in most of the tribal areas.

The Rhodesian security forces were permanently engaged, and based at Joint Operations Command Centres (JOCs) throughout the country.

All physically fit white, coloured and Asian men were required to participate in some form of military or police national service. The initial one-year call-up for training and

2 Stick: Four to six man unit or combat group

9

operational duty had been followed by a series of further call-ups for military service. As the war intensified, their call-ups increased in length and frequency until many men of military age spent as much time on call-up as they did on their ordinary jobs and professions. This caused massive disruption to family life and to business.

Bringing up young children with our husbands frequently away was not easy. By 5 pm we needed adult conversation and fathers to take over. Inevitably, when Larry was away, the car would break down and Sean would fall out of a tree again. We'd have another tooth to put under his pillow for the tooth fairy to collect. Brian's fourth birthday came and went without Larry being there to help me design and construct his birthday cake (a train) and to watch him ride the pony we'd hired for the afternoon.

"Jennifer is going to be late today," said Nina, who was our hostess that June. "Her husband was involved in a land mine incident two days ago. He's all right, thank God."

We were all shocked. It wasn't easy to focus on reviewing books after that news.

I'd recently read "The Siege of Krishnapur" by J.G. Farrell. The author had commented that the most interesting thing that had happened in his lifetime was the decline of the British Empire - something we could relate to in Rhodesia. It was evident that the British hadn't understood the Indians any better than they'd understood the Africans.

Margaret had also been impressed.

"The Collector in Krishnapur – he's the equivalent of our District Commissioner - is the only person in the area to anticipate the trouble brewing that culminates in the Indian Mutiny. He orders a deep trench to be dug around the perimeter of the Residency compound 'for drainage during the monsoon'. Those who remark on his eccentric behaviour are oblivious to the warning signs. During the siege, some rise to the occasion, others do not. There are bizarre descriptions. For example, an incident where the survivors load the cannon with anything they can lay their hands on: stones, penknives, embossed silver cutlery and even some false teeth."

Veronica nodded in agreement. "J.G. Farrell was extremely talented. Unfortunately, he died six years after winning the Booker Prize. He was writing a sequel to 'The Siege of Krishnapur' which he was going to call 'The Hill Station'. He never finished the book."

We were always amazed at the extent of Veronica's general knowledge.

Nina was reading "The Far Pavilions". She thought it was probably a lighter and more romantic read than J.G. Farrell's story of the mutiny.

Pam tended to confine herself to Wilbur Smith, Frederick Forsyth and Ken Follett. She wasn't very adventurous. Books about India in the nineteenth century didn't appeal to her.

Jennifer arrived. She played hockey for Matabeleland and we all envied her trim figure and muscular legs. Today she looked tense and pale.

We bombarded her with questions. Had Tom recovered from the contact? Had they found the terrorists responsible for the attack? Was she OK? How had she heard the news? Were the kids upset? After hugging all of us, she sat down with a sigh, and Nina brought her a cup of tea.

We waited for her to compose herself.

"They were travelling along a dirt road in the bush near Mount Darwin," she began. "Their five ton Bedford was carrying three PATU sticks. Most of the guys were squatting on the sandbags protecting the bed of the truck, and a few of them were sitting on the sides of the vehicle. It was midday, hellishly hot, and they were being hassled by swarms of mopani bees. They'd been patrolling an area where terrorists had been sighted, but there hadn't been any contacts. They were on their way back to camp, and looking forward to a hot shower and a few beers.

Suddenly, there was a massive explosion and the back of the truck was lifted about ten feet in the air. Luckily, it didn't roll.

There was an enormous hole where the road had been. The sandbags had protected most of them from the worst of the blast, thank goodness. Their ears were popping and ringing, but no one was seriously hurt.

Tom realised that his best mate Kaydee was missing – he was one of the guys who had been sitting on the side of the truck - so he jumped out to look for him. He was stiff and sore and limping a bit and he wasn't really thinking straight.

One of the other guys grabbed him and stopped him from going any farther. Terrorists could be hiding in the bush. So they checked the area first to make sure that an ambush hadn't been set up.

Kaydee had landed face down in some long grass, just missing a thorn bush. He'd obviously been concussed, and was moaning softly. Denis, the medic, examined him and said that he'd also broken his arm. He was bruised and bleeding, but otherwise didn't seem too bad. They called in a helicopter to casevac[3] him out. Another truck was sent to fetch them, and several hours later, they arrived safely at the camp."

Jen sighed shakily, as she finished relating the story. "Thank God they're all OK. Tom says the worst part was waiting to be picked up. It was so quiet. Even the birds seemed to have been frightened off. Kaydee's in hospital, but there's nothing seriously wrong with him. His arm's in plaster and he's badly scratched and bruised and obviously very shocked. He'll go home next week. Just as well. His wife's having their second child."

We were quiet for a while.

I knew that Larry was on patrol in Matabeleland North near Binga. Obviously he couldn't tell me exactly where.

Our husbands were in danger each time they were called up. It was very scary. We women lived our normal, ordinary, humdrum lives in the city. While they were out in the bush on patrol, at any moment, without warning, they could come under fire. In a second a land mine could sever their limbs. A crocodile could emerge from the water and drag someone off a riverbank. They could catch malaria and die before reaching hospital. They could be bitten by tsetse flies.

In Africa the list was endless.

3 Casevac: Casualty evacuation.

INDEPENDENCE: 1980

I remember exactly where I was on Tuesday, 4 March 1980 when we heard the news.

So does every other white Rhodesian.

Two other teachers and I were in Gifford High School's art room, the most relaxed place in the school. During art classes, the students were allowed to talk and listen to music. We all had a free period at this time of day, and were waiting for the promised announcement on the radio. Although we were apprehensive, we were expecting to hear that Bishop Abel Muzorewa had won the election and that he would possibly form a coalition with Joshua Nkomo.

The result was a total shock.

ZANU, Robert Mugabe's party, had won fifty-seven seats (an outright majority) in the 100-seat parliament. Nkomo's ZAPU had won twenty seats and Bishop Muzorewa's party, the United African National Council (UANC), three. We had been fighting Marxist terrorists for years, and now this 'activist' was to be our leader. It was absolutely shattering, because it was completely unexpected. No one had been prepared for such an eventuality. The media (sometimes referred to as 'Ian Smith's propaganda machine' by the unconverted) had assured us that Zimbabwe-Rhodesia would more or less effortlessly become the Republic of Zimbabwe with the Bishop at the helm.

Lessons were forgotten as the school began to hum with hundreds of agitated voices.

"What will happen to us?"

"We'd better head for Beit Bridge right now."

"Mugabe will want revenge."

"My Dad's in the Selous Scouts. He's shot three gooks. We're going to have to gap it[4] for sure."

---

4 'Gapping it' or 'taking the gap' – colloquialism used by whites meaning 'to leave'.

"There'll be no future for us here with a commie government in power."

"Oh, God, I sent our passports to Jo'burg to be renewed last week. What are we going to do?"

During the course of the day, news filtered through of mobs in Salisbury's[5] townships chanting jubilantly and dancing in the streets, and of riot police at the ready with tear gas. Rumour had it that the police and the army in Bulawayo were burning all sorts of documents. Panic and fear made teaching impossible. We all wanted to get home to our families. Decisions would have to be made.

At the next Book Club, we compared notes.

"I was having tea at Haddon's," said Nina. "The restaurant's radio was switched on for the announcement, and there was absolute silence when the news was broadcast to the nation. Then everyone began to talk at once. Most of the people there were women, and they were in a complete state. Those with small children at nursery school or playgroup rushed off to fetch them at once. I don't know what they thought would happen to their kids.

I went home immediately to phone Ian at work, as I knew he would be anxious. He'd got there before me and was phoning all our friends to try to find out where I was. He gave me hell for not telling him where I was going. 'Today might be the beginning of a totally altered life-style in this country,' he told me. 'We may not be able to stay here.'"

Nina's husband adored her and liked to know exactly where she was every moment of the day. He was big, burly and bombastic. She was tiny and usually gentle, except when religion was an issue. She went to mass every day, their two boys were altar servers and she ran the catechetical committee on the parish council.

"I had some friends for tea," said Lisa. "We'd heard the news and were discussing what was likely to happen. I went

5 The name of the capital city was changed to 'Harare' on 18 April 1982 – the second anniversary of Zimbabwean Independence.

into the kitchen to fetch some more biscuits. Happiness and the gardener didn't know I was there. They were outside the back door dancing about, clapping their hands and congratulating one another. I was dumb-founded. Just the previous day, I'd been talking to them about the Bishop, and we were all agreeing that he was a good man and that he would do great things for the country. I didn't say anything to them and they didn't see me."

Pamela began to tremble, as she recounted her experience. "I was pushing Sandy's pram down Selborne Avenue on my way to buy flowers outside the City Hall. Suddenly, I found that I had been surrounded by a bunch of young black guys. I began to get really scared, as they were chanting 'Mugabe! Mugabe! Mugabe!' I didn't know what to do. I picked Sandy up and she began to cry. I think this saved me from being attacked, as other people in the street realised what was going on and came to my rescue. 'White bitch!' the blacks shouted before they ran away. It was awful. I've been having nightmares ever since."

Pam rummaged in her bag for a tissue.

The name "Mugabe" made us all feel nervous. But what was really terrifying was the fact that this incident had happened to poor Pam in broad daylight on one of the busiest streets in Bulawayo. Where were the police?

Rachel brought Pam a glass of water, put her arm around her and offered her a cigarette. The two of them lit up, and Pam gradually became calmer.

"The bastards," said Rachel. "You'd think they'd be grateful for all the hospitals and schools we whites have built for them. You'd think they'd appreciate the civilising influence we've had. *Our* soldiers haven't been out there in the bush cutting off the lips and ears of so-called 'informers'. You'd think they'd want law and order, wouldn't you? But, no, they want Comrade Mugabe, a bloody communist, a pawn of Russia and China."

Since 4 March, everyone had been concerned about the effect of the new government on the police and the army. Would there be one law for blacks and another for whites now?

"Something very different happened to me," said Veronica. "I was in Sanders buying a new school uniform for Gwen. The results had been announced, and I was shattered. I felt really ill at ease at first, as the shop assistants were all black. They were very subdued, though, so I asked them how they felt. Two of the women burst into tears. 'We had expected Nkomo, Father Zimbabwe, to lead our nation. Who is this Jongwe? Who is this rooster? What will happen to us Ndebeles when the Shonas are in charge? There will be war between Mashonaland and Matabeleland.' They were in a state of shock, too."

On 3 September 1978, a civilian aircraft, the "Hunyani" had been shot down by a heat-seeking Sam 7 missile. There were 56 people on board. Eighteen people survived. Ten of these survivors were massacred at the crash site by ZIPRA soldiers. Eight escaped.

On 12 February 1979 a second viscount, the "Umniati" was shot down. This time there were no survivors. The "Umniati" crashed 50km north-east of the spot where the "Hunyani" had been brought down a few months earlier.

We had been outraged. Nkomo's terrorists had killed 59 people, most of them white holiday-makers on their way back to Salisbury from Kariba. Lt.-Gen. Peter Walls, Commander of Combined Operations, was Nkomo's target in the case of the "Umniati". He and his wife had spent the weekend at Kariba. They were among the passengers on a later plane.

In spite of this, everyone would have preferred a Muzorewa/ Nkomo coalition. We regarded Nkomo as a moderate and Mugabe as a doctrinaire communist, although we knew so little about him.

"I'm sure you all saw Mugabe's address to the nation," said Margaret. "He's obviously a very well-educated man, extremely articulate and intelligent. He didn't come across as the monster I expected, yelling abuse at the whites and crowing about his victory. Instead, he talked about 'reconciliation' not 'recrimination' and about 'turning swords into ploughshares'. He assured us whites that there was a place for us in the new Zimbabwe. I was so overcome with emotion and relief that I began to cry. He named David Smith Minister of Commerce and Industry and Denis Norman Minister of Agriculture. Those two are RF through and through, rigidly pro white, and Mugabe must be well aware of it. But he obviously realises that he needs to draw on their expertise. Matthew and I feel very encouraged."

We'd heard of the odd family who had high-tailed it to The Bridge, with the intention of crossing the border into South Africa at the slightest sign of trouble. Beit Bridge Hotel had been jam-packed for a couple of nights. Most had come back, we'd heard, prepared to 'wait and see' once again. 'Waiting and seeing' had long been the way of life for whites living in Rhodesia.

Jen had brought a copy of a fascinating document her husband Tom had obtained. It was not exactly top secret, but it certainly could be described as highly sensitive. It was an excerpt from a report allegedly written *before the election* by one of the British election supervisors in charge of a rural area in the east of the country. He was commenting on the way he believed the black people would vote.

He reported that families had held discussions and that kraal heads had met. It was agreed that people would vote for ZANU because the people wanted peace. Mugabe had demonstrated that only he could end the war. If the war ended, families could be re-united, because Mugabe would bring 'the boys' back. If he failed to win they would have to return to Mozambique.

The Bishop had had a chance but had failed to make any difference to power structure. Marxism was not an issue, he said. The people knew little about it. What they did know about was European domination which Muzorewa had accepted, but which Mugabe would end. The people had had enough of being ruled by a small white minority.

"He went on to observe," Jen continued, "that although the presence of guerrillas in the area would perhaps, through intimidation, have increased the ZANU vote by about 10%, this was not particularly significant in his estimation. He felt that the vote was the authentic voice of the African people."

"Have we all been taken for a ride?" I said. "Or have we been ridiculously naïve? Could Ian Smith really have thought that the Bishop was going to win, and that the Rhodesian Front would continue to manipulate political affairs? Let's face it, the Bishop would, to some extent, have been an RF puppet. Every radio broadcast and every television programme leading up to the election indicated that the transition would be smooth and peaceful. The Bishop, a 'Man of God' and a 'Man of Peace', would be totally opposed to any bloodshed or violence. How could we all have been so wrong?"

"Propaganda," remarked Veronica "is incredibly powerful and insidious. People, who have ideas and concepts drummed into their heads twenty-four hours of every day, will obviously come to believe the information they are fed. Look at Nazi Germany. Remember 'Nineteen Eighty-Four'? Every single aspect of life was controlled by the Party. In our case 'The Party' has been the RF. Perhaps we shouldn't blame ourselves too much for being gullible. Perhaps we should consider whether or not we've been betrayed."

Rachel said nothing.

Like many other white Rhodesians, she had a large photo of Ian Smith in her lounge.

There was very little time for book reviews after this. The Zimbabwe we'd been hoping for was not going to be. Instead, the future was likely to be precarious and unpredictable. We would face the weeks ahead with trepidation. Would we all still be here this time next year, or even next month?

DIVORCE

Ironically, Veronica was the first person from our Book Club to emigrate a couple of years after Zimbabwe celebrated its independence.

Book Club was at Lisa's that month. Jennifer was reviewing a book by C. Emily Dibb, who came from Bulawayo.

"'Ivory, Apes and Peacocks' is a most enjoyable read," began Jennifer. "I'm sure you'll all recall learning the poem 'Cargoes' by John Masefield at school. Remember the exotic cargo that the Quinquireme of Nineveh was bringing back to Palestine from 'distant Ophir'?

There's an account of a swarm of bees, disturbed by the chiming of the City Hall clock, one hot October day. The author describes how they attack everything in sight from a team of mules and their muleteer to a middle-aged bachelor in an immaculate white linen suit. It's hilarious."

Larry and I had bought a house in Matsheumhlope, the same suburb where Emily Dibb's family had lived. Our property was at the end of a quiet road. We had a large garden and a swimming pool – it was a perfect place for young children. There was bush all around us, but snakes were not our worst problem. Sometimes in October, when the heat was stifling, our neighbour's bees would go crazy, and we'd have to spend the entire day inside, while they smashed against the windows intent on finding a way in.

He wasn't too concerned. They'll come home when it's dark, he'd say.

"That very incident was set as a comprehension exercise for a Junior Certificate English exam this week," I remarked. "What a coincidence. I was impressed with the examiners' choice. It was exactly the sort of piece the boys could get their teeth into. It isn't often that a local author's work is chosen. We can all relate to names like Reg Hart and Downing's Bakery. And I can certainly relate to angry bees."

Loud screams from the garden interrupted the next review. Lisa was in the process of recommending "Flowers in the Attic" as an excellent read. It sounded horrific to me – four children had been imprisoned in an attic by their mother and grandmother...

Lisa looked exasperated. "Where's Happiness? That girl is never around when you need her. Happiness! Happiness!"

She went out onto the veranda.

"Happiness! Damn it, where are you?"

"David's got his finger stuck in the door," called Sean.

David, Lisa's son, was obviously in pain. He was screaming more loudly than ever. A group of interested children had gathered round the shed. Several of us leapt to our feet to go to his assistance, but, as far as Lisa was concerned, Happiness was *paid* to handle this sort of thing. Her guests were there to relax.

"Happiiiii-nessssssssssss!"

Happiness came tearing round the corner, her cheeks bulging, a mug in her hand.

"Sorry, madam. Sorry, madam," she said. "Me and Joseph we were having our tea."

"Can't you see that David's got his finger stuck," shouted Lisa. "Help him quickly."

Happiness must have been one of the busiest maids in Bulawayo. She spent hours baking cakes and biscuits, making endless trays of tea and answering that little bell Lisa always had beside her.

Pam had been very quiet. She found it difficult to speak at first.

Then she said, "Girls, I'm getting divorced. I've been unhappy for a long time. I'm tired of his drinking and womanising. I'm sick of being hit. I've had enough of the embarrassment of going to work wearing dark glasses."

We looked at one another. We had often wondered about Pam's relationship with her husband, Adrian. He'd appeared pleasant enough when we'd seen him with Pam and Sandra. But we had noticed that Pam often seemed moody, and that her reviews were frequently sketchy and vague. We'd wondered whether she really enjoyed Book Club.

"Pam, dear," said Nina, "we care about you. If you don't want to talk about your problems, then that's fine. But if you want to tell us what has been going on, we're here to listen. Sometimes it helps to talk."

Nina had, with her usual tact and concern, voiced the feelings of the group. We all murmured words of encouragement and sympathy.

Pam smiled shakily. "Thank you. If you'll bear with me, I *would* like to tell you what has been going on. I don't know how much sense I'll make. But here goes...

I've thought for some time that he's been having an affair. I've actually been spying on him. It sounds sordid, I know, but I've wanted to catch him out. My sister and I have been doing our James Bond stuff as a team. We put Sandy in the car (she doesn't wake up usually, and if she does, she goes to sleep again almost immediately) and we drive about past his usual haunts like BAC and OM's and check the car park for his truck. Two nights ago, we saw him coming out of Queen's with a woman. He'd obviously been drinking with her. They were weaving about with their arms around each other trying to find his truck. We followed them back to her place.

We gave them a few minutes before knocking on the door of her flat. We could hear sounds of giggling and scuffling and then the woman opened the door. We introduced ourselves and I asked to see Adrian. She tried to slam the door, but I managed to push her aside and we shoved our way in. There he was, pathetic creep, half undressed, hiding behind the door. We'd caught him red-handed, and I had a witness. I didn't say a word. I just stared at him, and then the two of us left.

I went to see a lawyer the next day. I've moved in with my sister and my parents. They never liked him, anyway. Fortunately Sandy knows nothing, except that her Dad and I are getting a divorce. I've been surprised at how few questions she's asked. It makes you realise that children understand more than you're aware of."

We told her that we were sure she'd be better off on her own, especially since her family was so supportive.

Pam fell back in her chair, relieved that the strain of pretending to be happily married was over. She'd been sitting on the edge of her seat, while recounting her story.

Veronica broke the news of her imminent departure quietly.

"Graham has been transferred to Durban," she said. "It's a promotion. We are very sad about leaving, but this step up his corporate ladder is extremely important. Ultimately, we expect to return to the UK after the Durban stint. I'd like the girls to go to university there."

"Oh, no, not another person leaving," wailed Jen. "Can't you wait a while longer to see how things go here? It's beginning to look as though Robert Mugabe intends to run the country sensibly and democratically. Can't you give it a little more time?"

Veronica smiled and shook her head. "We're already committed to the transfer to South Africa. It's a wonderful opportunity for Graham. I am going to miss all of you, of course. I've loved Book Club. But you won't have any difficulty replacing me. I know lots of girls who would love to be invited to join this group."

"It's OK for some," said Rachel bleakly. "Fine if you've got plenty of money and British passports. Some of us are stuck here, whether we like it or not."

"Imagine living in a place where you have to do your own housework," said Lisa. You simply become a drudge. No tennis, no bridge, no tea in town with your friends. No maid to look after the kids when you want to go out at night. Gapping it is not for me. Think how you'll miss our way of life. The braais[6] and the beer; watching the sun set from a houseboat on Kariba; skiing on Ncema Dam... I'll be here until the lights go out... In fact, I'll probably switch them off myself!"

---

6 Braai – abbreviation of braaivleis – the South African and Zimbabwean equivalent of a barbeque. (From Afrikaans: "braai" meaning "roast" and "vleis" meaning "meat".)

Often, people who were staying tried to make those who were leaving feel guilty. You were letting the side down. Snide comments were frequently muttered out of the corners of mouths about rats abandoning sinking ships.

Veronica was too astute to allow herself to be sucked into an argument and too sensible to be upset by Rachel's remarks. As far as she was concerned, there was no need for justification or explanation.

DISINTEGRATION

Veronica and her family settled happily in Durban quite close to the sea. Graham loved his job and the girls were doing very well at their new school. Then one day, completely out of the blue, two masked intruders broke into her house and viciously attacked her in her own kitchen. We heard that she had been stabbed several times. Somehow, bleeding badly, she managed to drag herself down the hill to the road, and was able to stop a passing motorist. She was rushed to hospital, and, thank God, she survived. Not long after that and not surprisingly, they returned to the UK, and we lost touch with them.

She had been the stabilising force in our Book Club.

Some months after she'd left, a number of members decided that preparing reviews and writing them out, so that they could be left in the books for others to read was too much like hard work.

"Why don't we just say whether or not we liked a book?" said Rachel. "I can't be bothered with feeling obliged to write my views down. It's like being back at school. We should be able to relax on a Saturday morning and feel free to chat."

"I quite agree," said Louise. "I don't like being told to do things. And I don't like analysing everything I read."

"I actually think it would be much more convenient to have Book Club in the evening," remarked Jennifer. "I need to go shopping on Saturdays. I don't get much chance during the week"

"Yes, count me in for an evening session," said Lisa. "David's in the cricket team and we like to watch him play on Saturdays. I'd far rather have Book Club in the evenings."

Pam hadn't been to Book Club for ages. We'd heard that she had been offered a job in Harare. We'd also heard rumours that she'd found a new man. Nina was away again. Ian travelled frequently, and she accompanied him on his business trips whenever she could. She'd told me that she didn't have much time to read any more, and she felt that she was letting the group down since she was seldom able to attend meetings. "Book Club is too serious," insisted Rachel. "I think we should get together for tea and a chat and make it more of a social activity. Of course it's nice to talk about the books we've read, but we don't have to go into such detail. We could just indicate whether a book is 'a good read' or 'a poor one'."

"I don't like having to choose in rotation," said Louise. "I think we should be able to take two or three books at a time. It wouldn't take so long then. I could get home earlier."

Some of us who had been in the group since it began were determined that Book Club would not be hi-jacked. One feature that made our Book Club special and, in fact, unique in Bulawayo, we were sure, was our desire to discuss books, explore their value and branch out into reading different authors.

"I totally disagree with you, Rachel," said Shirley. "Book reviews are important, and an integral part of this Book Club. Without them, we might as well go to the library."

Shirley, who had joined the group recently, usually had a calming effect. Like many of us, she felt that Book Club was an excellent forum for discussion. Reviews sent us off on all sorts of interesting and unexpected tangents. Small and slim with wavy blond hair and handsome features, she always looked well-groomed, even on a Saturday, when most of us slopped about in jeans and T-shirts. With a clear, carrying voice and a commanding presence that belied her stature, she was able to discipline even the naughtiest classes without any apparent effort.

"And while we are about it," she said, "Margaret and I get really irritated at the way some of you arrive half an hour or three-quarters of an hour late for Book Club. As a matter of courtesy, everyone should make the effort to arrive on time."

For a few moments, there was a surprised and rather shocked silence as people digested this comment.

"As regards shopping on Saturday," said Marilyn, "you simply need to organise yourself a little better on the first

Saturday of the month. Go shopping earlier. Book Club starts at 10 o'clock. Surely you could manage to get things done in two hours, Jennifer? "

Like Shirley, Marilyn was petite and fashion-conscious. She'd been a finalist for "Miss Rhodesia" some years before. At the moment, her hair was blonde. The picture of health and vitality, she normally spent several hours a day at the gym or at the swimming pool, and was a perfect shade of bronze from careful sun tanning. Right now, though, she was very pregnant with her second child. She was a late-starter, having had several miscarriages.

"An evening Book Club wouldn't be convenient for me," said Margaret. "Matthew doesn't like me driving around at night. I think we should continue as we are with Saturday morning meetings."

"I'm not an intellectual," said Rachel, "and I often feel that those of you who are teachers think you're superior to us secretaries and book keepers."

So this was what it was really about.

We weren't sorry to see some of the members leave.

An element of bitchiness and competition had crept in. 'I bake better than you do.' 'You've got more money than we've got.' 'I spent a whole day in the kitchen and you bought only two cakes and a few sausage rolls.' 'I served imported wine at my Book Club and you only gave us local.'

The trappings had become important for some.

Louise (a very new member) had really irritated us with her trade union mentality. On a recent occasion, parents had been asked to bring cakes for a fund-raising effort at our children's school. Louise, an 'ex-pat' from the UK, objected on the grounds that she paid school fees. Why should she do anything extra?

We wanted a supportive circle of intelligent friends all of whom had the same agenda. This entailed observing certain rules and being disciplined in the way we functioned.

In future we would be more selective about new members. We were determined that Book Club would continue to be something we looked forward to each month.

Part II

MATURING

1984 – 1999

Choices

I left teaching in December 1984.

The prescribed texts for English literature exams were beginning to reflect a very different outlook. The Ministry of Education advocated the study of books that celebrated African customs and traditions, as opposed to decadent western culture, which bore little or no relevance to life in liberated Zimbabwe. In other words: "A Son of the Soil" not "Hamlet". History had already been re-written. The new source material eulogised the magnificent achievements of the country's revolutionary freedom fighters and demonised the whites. Marxism was enthusiastically embraced.

Teaching wasn't for me anymore.

I was offered a job as the Bulawayo area sales representative for a Harare company that produced promotional material. I found working on a commission-only basis very different from having the security of a regular salary, but, as I gained confidence, I began to enjoy the challenges, and the adrenaline surge that followed a successful sale.

My hours were flexible, and I was able to spend more time watching Sean and Brian swimming and playing hockey and tennis. I could also do more to help with their school's fund-raising activities.

It wasn't all about brilliant sales, though. There were always delivery and quality problems and there were frequent errors and disputes. This was the competitive, cut and thrust world of commerce, not the sheltered, insular world of teaching.

Black people now had more money and more status. They were buying houses in traditionally white areas and sending their children to schools that had formerly been white. With the emergence of this new middle class, a natural integration was taking place.

The white community continued to shrink. The economy was taking strain, as efficiency in every sector deteriorated, and bribery and corruption became more blatant. Foreign currency was difficult to source. Confidence in the justice system and in law and order was evaporating. Many predicted a dismal future.

Others felt that as long as health and education were of a high standard, they'd hang on a little longer... Drugs in our schools (apart from the odd stash of marijuana here and there) were virtually non-existent. Discipline was an integral part of our education system. We preferred our children strictly controlled, well-mannered and drug-free.

But independence had not brought the peace and stability we'd been promised.

Mugabe and Nkomo had been locked in a power struggle since 1980. There had always been rivalry between the ZIPRA and ZANLA armies, and this had made integration of the two wings of the struggle into the National Army virtually impossible. Mugabe insisted that Nkomo's ZAPU party was plotting to overthrow ZANU. Arms caches had been discovered all over the country as evidence of this. (Of course, these could have been planted to implicate Nkomo.) The Ndebele people had to be shown who was in charge. This was Mugabe's rationale for sending the Fifth Brigade (a North-Korean trained unit) into Matabeleland to carry out a systematic reign of terror, known as the Gukurahundi (Shona for "the early rain which washes away the chaff before the spring rains"). Ndebele people were slaughtered, raped, abducted and starved. Bodies were thrown down wells and disused mine shafts. Domestic animals were butchered and homes burnt. The genocide was carried out in remote rural areas; where between 10,000 and 30,000 civilians were massacred. Obviously, the recording of atrocities was not in the regime's interests.

We'd heard rumours that dreadful things were happening out in the bush. But it was difficult to know what to believe or who to blame, since Ndebele militants (or dissidents) were (we were told) responsible for attacks on white farmers and government representatives in Matabeleland and parts of the Midlands, and for the destruction of government property.

Larry and I had been awakened one February night in 1981, by loud gunfire and explosions. At first we'd thought it was thunder. We'd grabbed Sean and Brian and huddled together in the shower (the safest place in the house) until the bombardment stopped. Amazingly, the kids didn't wake up, although it sounded as if our garden was the centre of the war zone. A pitched battle between ZIPRA and ZANLA was being fought near the Hilltop Motel on the main Harare/Bulawayo road, a kilometre from our house in Kumalo.

That was the closest I'd come to any action.

Others had been less fortunate.

When Marian, her husband, Jerry and their two girls moved from town to Olive Tree Farm, she resigned from Book Club. Everyone had liked her. She had that quality of gentle, calm assurance many religious people have.

They were members of a group of white missionaries who'd founded the Pentecostal Community of Reconciliation at Olive Tree Farm and the adjoining New Adam Farm near Esigodeni, a small village 43km from Bulawayo. They took none of the usual security measures other farmers employed: the barbed-wire fences; the armed guards; the floodlights. They led simple lives of service: preaching the word of God and teaching the local people better farming techniques.

On Thursday 26 November 1987, sixteen people from Olive Tree Farm and New Adam Farm were bound and then hacked to death by a group of machete-wielding peasants singing revolutionary songs. Four men, five women and seven children were savagely slaughtered. Among them were Marian, Jerry, their two girls and their eighteen-month-old son. Two children escaped.

Who was responsible for this barbaric, utterly senseless act? Were these murderers Ndebele dissidents attacking white soft targets to attract international attention in order to discredit the government? Or were they government personnel masquerading as dissidents to harm Joshua Nkomo's reputation? It was common knowledge that a group of squatters had had disagreements with the missionaries about land and grazing rights. Their leader was a notorious dissident known as Gayigusu.

The City Hall was packed for the memorial service, which everyone from Book Club attended. Missionary colleagues spoke eloquently of their courage and commitment and of their love for God. Their pastors hailed them as martyrs and asked us to pray that God would forgive their murderers. That was what they would have wanted.

Andrew Meldrum, a respected journalist, wrote of the "blood-drenched bedroom" at Olive Tree Farm and of burnt bodies at New Adam Farm. He wrote about the slaughter of an infant - a six-week-old baby boy.

We remembered those who had died in the dreadful Elim Massacre in the Eastern Highlands on 23 June 1978. Eight British Pentecostal missionaries and four young children (the youngest was a three-week old baby) were bayoneted to death by terrorists. Most of the women had been raped. There was a photograph of a mother lying with her baby beside her. They'd been bludgeoned to death. Their arms were reaching out towards one another.

Nine years later, we were still asking God to forgive murderers.

On 22 December 1987 Mugabe and Nkomo signed the Unity Accord, which effectively swallowed ZAPU. The two factions combined to become ZANU PF. The Unity Accord created a one-party state with Joshua Nkomo assuming the role of the country's second Vice President. Many Ndebeles felt marginalised - even betrayed - by their revered Father Zimbabwe. This, as far as they were concerned, was surrender.

As a result of the Unity Accord, Mugabe declared an amnesty.

The presidential pardon resulted in the release of 75 members of the security forces charged or convicted of offences relating to human rights abuses. All those "dissidents" still in the bush who surrendered by the end of May would also be pardoned. Morgan Sango Nkomo (Gayigusu), the man allegedly responsible for butchering sixteen blameless missionaries, who'd devoted their lives to helping black people, took advantage of the offer and was declared a free man.

The civil war was over, at last, and the political instability brought to an end.

The 1990s, much to everyone's relief, were a quieter period in the history of Zimbabwe.

STRONG WOMEN

"I've just read the most enthralling book," said Colleen. She was sitting on a sofa beside two large mounds of grey fluff that were Jo's Persian cats.

"My sister in Vancouver sent it to me. Inside was a note: 'Trust me – you'll love it!' She knows me so well, you see. I was hooked before I'd reached the bottom of the first page. Dolores Claiborne, a woman in her sixties, has just been read her rights. She's not intimidated, though. Far from it. Using lively, often derisive banter, she outmanoeuvres the two policemen attempting to question her. It's obvious from the outset that she's the dominant character in the interview room.

After reading a few pages, I realised that it's a monologue. There are no chapters - no divisions at all. Dolores imposes her will and her personality on the reader as well as on the policemen and the stenographer. Her tale is utterly compelling. To hell with the supper. Too bad about 3B's comprehensions. You keep turning the pages. Just a few minutes more..."

Colleen had been a professional actress when she was younger. She knew exactly what to do to hold her audience's attention.

"She claims that she did not kill 'that stupid bitch Vera'. But she did, she admits, kill her husband in the summer of '63. She paints a vivid picture of what it was like to be the wife of despicable Joe St George and the housekeeper/companion of Vera Donovan. Her description of her relationship with her late employer is as riveting as her account of the circumstances that drove her to kill her husband.

Vera reminds me of Mrs Dubose, the elderly lady that Jem and Scout encounter in 'To Kill a Mockingbird'. They're both domineering and repellent most of the time, and then, completely unexpectedly, we're given glimpses of admirable qualities."

"You haven't told us who the author is," said Marilyn.

"My sister knows I hate stories about weird creatures with telepathic powers. That's why I was so surprised when I saw Stephen King's name on the cover."

"Who wrote it?" asked Margaret leaning forward in her chair.

"Stephen King," said Colleen.

"I loved Dolores," said Shirley. "What a gutsy woman. She's so sassy and resourceful. And I'm impressed that a man can appreciate what it's like to hang wet sheets on the line using six pegs (never just four) in the freezing cold and what it's like having to clean up copious amounts of 'shit'."

"I've changed my opinion of Stephen King," said Jo. "I've always known that he's hugely popular and a master of the suspense thriller. But I'm not into horror stories. I want to read about real people in real situations. Dolores is a real person. I feel that I'm actually in that interview room with her. 'Everything I did, I did for love,' she says. And you want to leap to your feet and give her a standing ovation."

It was a month later. Most of us had read "Dolores Claiborne" and had already ranked it among the year's best books.

"She's on my list of the fascinating women in literature," said Colleen.

"Like Tess," said Marilyn. "And Elizabeth Bennet, of course."

"Miss Havisham and Jane Eyre," said Diana.

"Portia," said Shirley. "I love 'The Quality of Mercy'."

I'd inherited my mother's admiration for Anne Shirley. Anne with an e.

While I was considering whether to admit to this, it struck me that Margaret hadn't said a word.

"Who's your favourite?" I asked her.

"Pardon?" she said.

"Who's your favourite?"

"My what?"

"Your favourite female character."

"Oh. I'd say Hester Prynne. Elizabeth Bennet, naturally. And I love the Wife of Bath."

During tea I asked Shirley what was wrong with Margaret. She seemed distant and unfocused.

"She's going deaf," said Shirley sadly. "She can't hear much of what's being discussed. I've begged her to tell everyone. But she says she's embarrassed. She's thinking of leaving book club. She says she's becoming a liability."

I was shocked.

When she finally did tell us, we managed to convince her that we needed her more than she needed us. We promised that we'd make an effort to look at her directly when we spoke to her so that she could try to lip-read. She explained that she felt the urge to run outside when she was assaulted by the pounding waves of our exuberant chatter.

It had been some time since we'd written out our reviews as a matter of routine. While I'd always found it easier to record my impressions, some of the ladies could comment on what they'd read quite adequately from memory. We decided from then on to make an effort to jot down our thoughts, so that Margaret could follow our reviews. She told us that things became much easier if she had "context". When she had an idea of the subject, it was much easier to work out what was probably being said, and then focus on picking up a few key words.

Her condition, and our dawning understanding and appreciation of it, drew us closer as a group.

Larry and I now had our own business, Alfa (Pvt.) Limited. Towards the end of November 1994, I'd been notified by our Harare manager that the company I'd been with for nearly ten years would be shutting down shortly before Christmas.

We'd always wanted to do our own thing, so we decided to make an offer.

We mortgaged the house; borrowed the money we needed and, within a few weeks, we owned a business that produced calendars, diaries and corporate gifts with its head office in

Bulawayo. The bulk of our sales would come from Harare, so we crammed eight reps and an admin manager into a tiny office in Harare's central business district.

During our very precarious first year, we'd had to work from home. Our bedroom bulged with folders of film and filing cabinets containing customers' artwork and company information. The despatch department operated from the lounge. Cartons were stacked in piles that reached towards the ceiling. Packing materials spilled onto the floor. Rolls of gummed tape and consignment pads replaced the vase of flowers on the coffee table.

Larry and I had moved to Sean's room and the two boys found themselves sharing a bedroom again for the first time in ages. They'd always got on very well, so it wasn't a problem. Brian was at the Bulawayo Polytechnic halfway through a graphic design course, while Sean was studying for a diploma in marketing management. Both boys were perfectly poised to work for Alfa. Larry had his management experience and accounting qualification. I had the sales experience and a working knowledge of printing.

That first year was a nightmare. Many of our suppliers let us down, reneging on agreements we'd made with them. We were swept into a vortex of disasters that ranged from late deliveries to mistakes on film and sub-standard printing. Larry handled irate customers far better than I did. He coped with the complaints and the pressure diplomatically and professionally. I fled the house as early as possible each morning to visit suppliers, and to escape those incessantly ringing phones.

Somehow we got through it.

Our house became a home again in our second year of business, when we moved into premises in town and set up a screen-printing factory of our own.

Margaret was no longer an acquaintance whose intellect I respected. I was getting to know the strong, caring but vulnerable woman, who was trying hard to come to terms with an appalling sense of loss. For several months we'd been writing letters to one another.

She missed the simple conversations she'd had with her children. "It's such an effort for me to understand and for them to try to make me comprehend what they're saying, that all spontaneity is lost," she told me. "I remember reading about another deaf person's experience of family meals. He said it was like being a dog under the table. You had to wait patiently until someone offered you a titbit. And then it wasn't necessarily the scrap you would have chosen ..."

I told her how much I dreaded having to shout at a deaf person (and at her specifically), in an effort to make the person hear and understand me. It seemed to me so impolite. I was sure that others felt the same and often avoided conversation for that reason. I knew that mine was one of the voices she found difficult. She seemed to be able to "hear" or at least follow what Shirley, Marilyn, Colleen and Jo said reasonably well.

She replied that for a long time she had pretended to hear and understand.

"I observed people closely, and if a question was posed (something I dreaded), I quickly tried to calculate whether they were expecting me to say 'yes' or 'no'. It was immediately obvious if I'd given the wrong answer. Their discomfort made me feel even more agitated. They'd repeat the question, and, more often than not, I still couldn't figure out what they were asking. Then...'It doesn't matter,' they'd say. I know people mean this kindly, but to a deaf person who has been trying with every fibre of her being to understand, it *does* matter, and that simple phrase feels like a door slamming in her face..."

We decided to have a note pad handy at our meetings so that the person sitting next to her could record snippets of conversation to give her the 'context' she needed. It was so rewarding to see her face light up, when she understood what the laughter had been about.

She was the first to review 'Memoirs of a Geisha' by Arthur Golden.

"A bidding contest is held for the apprentice geisha's deflowering. Sayuri is only fifteen years old at the time and completely innocent. The man who eventually wins the contest keeps vials of blood-soaked swabs from the 'encounters' he's had with other virgins. His case contains forty to fifty such vials.

I wish I knew more about anthropology. Perhaps then I would understand why so many cultures – if not all – have exploited female sexuality for the fantasy and pleasure of men."

This led to a discussion on female circumcision, especially as it is practised in Africa. Until women rose up en masse and refused to have their daughters subjected to barbaric rites, we agreed, they would continue to be abused and abased in this way.

Having been bowled over by 'How to Make an American Quilt', I tentatively suggested that we each write a short story. The response was tepid, to say the least!

"'A Letter to My Sister'," read Margaret, introducing the story I'd written, and looking around our Book Club circle to make sure that she had everyone's attention.

"A Letter to My Sister"

Do you remember Christmas Eve mornings when the earth was new? It always seemed to rain the night before. The grass sparkled with droplets lit by the early morning sun. White lilies, growing wild, shone fresh and pure. We called them "Solitudians" after our farm "Solitude" – we didn't know their real name. Everything was beautiful, so quiet, so peaceful. From the fields far away the faint, contented lowing of cattle filtered through the morning stillness.

We had a mission. It was to organise our Christmas tree. Not for us an effete fir tree – there was no such thing where we lived on our ranch in the Hartley area. Our tree would be much more interesting. We would use a branch cut from one of the beautiful indigenous trees close to the house. The exciting part, however, would be the gathering of the wild, trailing asparagus ferns we called "evergreen" with which we would drape it. We knew where to look for them.

There were puddles of water everywhere on the narrow farm road. We eased our bare feet into them, gasping a little, at first, at the cold shock that sent delicious tingles through our goose-pimply bodies. When we sloshed through to the middle, we paused for a few moments to let the velvet mud ooze languidly between our toes. It was bliss. Then on to the next puddle. Sometimes we would run through, splashing each other until we were splattered with muddy, grey splotches. It didn't matter. We were wearing our oldest clothes. We could change later when the evergreen had been gathered.

Further on, the bush on either side of the road became thicker. Nestled against the trunks of trees and growing in their shade and protection were our precious ferns. They were a different green from that of the trees and bushes around, and a different green from the lush grass. Our evergreen was bright emerald, and rain droplet jewels sparkled on the delicate fronds.

We drew our penknives and carefully cut the stems. Each was covered in thorns, so we tried to avoid too many scratches. But it was all part of the excitement, wasn't it? We piled our finds together in a clearing. Soon there was a green mound of fresh-smelling ferns, which grew and grew.

By now we were warmer. Birds were watching us, chattering in the trees, joyous and free. Did they know that Christmas was tomorrow?

Carl ran back to the barns to get a wheelbarrow. You and I sat down for a while on a rock, holding our heads back to catch the warmth of the sun on our faces. We talked quietly about what we hoped to find in our stockings and under the tree. There were long, succulent grass stalks around us. As we chatted, we pulled them out, one by one, and chewed the ends. They were tasty, rather like fresh salad straight from the ground.

Then you spotted one of our favourite insects. It was a gorgeous ruby-red creature, moving single-mindedly across a patch of earth near our rock. Together we squatted near it, and could not resist stroking it. It felt like velvet. We always thought it was some type of spider. Do you remember that, many years later, we learned it was a species of tick? A spider sounds much more benign than a parasitic tick.

Carl came back with the wheelbarrow and we carefully loaded our evergreen onto it. We took turns wheeling the barrow back down the farm track to the house. It was much hotter now and we were famished.

After breakfast and a bath, we went into the lounge to set about constructing our Christmas tree. Mum had chosen a suitable branch that was already "planted" in a tin in the far corner near the chimney. While we had been bathing, the cook had brought in the evergreen from the wheelbarrow outside.

What followed was, in our opinion, a work of art. We would pass stems of evergreen to our mother. She would entwine the branch with these, gradually interweaving them. The sharp ends of the stems vanished from sight and what slowly grew before our eyes was the loveliest, most desirable Christmas tree. It was roundish in shape, not pointed like your conventional Christmas tree with its neat, domesticated, well-behaved and very English shape. This was far less remote, far friendlier, a product of our efforts, born of our soil, a unique part of "Solitude".

We all stood back to admire it and to sniff its delicate, fresh scent. Mum went to fetch the box of ornaments from her cupboard. She placed it carefully on the carpet and we all knelt around it, filled with anticipation and consumed with impatience. Opening the box was like rediscovering treasure that had been buried and forgotten for a long time. Mum untied the string, lifted the lid and reverently removed the tissue paper and the thick layer of cotton wool that guarded our decorations.

There they were, all intact, just as entrancing as they had been last year. There was the pretty red teardrop with a diamond centre and there the iridescent peacock with its white spangled tail. There was the round blue sparkly ball and next to it, in its neat little cardboard compartment, the red and purple lozenge with its shimmering frost. Under this layer of decorations were the strands of tinsel. These were silver and gold ropes, thick and luxuriant, not the sparse strings you buy today. Under these again were the candles and holders. At the very bottom was a length of green crepe paper.

We started with the paper. Mum tied this round the tin. Now our tree stood in a green container. Then we passed her the ornaments, one by one. Using coloured thread, she tied each to an evergreen "branch". We were allowed to tie some onto the lower branches. Mum had to use a ladder to reach up to position the silver star at the top of the tree. We all helped twine the tinsel around the tree.

Finally the candles were fixed into the brass holders with their neat little claws. We had no electricity, and we had never heard of twinkling fairy lights that pulsated and flashed frenetically. Our candles glowed quietly and calmly with a promise of magic to come.

At last our tree was complete. Mum drew the curtains and slowly lit each candle so that we could breathe in Christmas for a few moments. We four stood together in contentment, looking up at the tree that we had created, shimmering in a delicate golden glow.

The miracle that was Christmas had begun."

Diana said she'd enjoyed my story. Jo said it took her back to the special Christmases she'd enjoyed as a child. Colleen said that it was a little different from Christmas in Belfast. Two or three ladies glanced at their watches. Surely it was tea-time?

In March 1999 Matthew took Margaret to South Africa. Tests indicated that what little was left of her hearing had deteriorated alarmingly. The specialist also had good news, though, much to their relief. She was a suitable candidate for a cochlear implant, and he agreed to do the procedure immediately.

She told us at Book Club some weeks after her operation that, although she couldn't hear everything, she could hear most things. Background noise was still a problem – it always would be - and she would never be able to use the telephone. But she would be able to have a normal conversation with her family again.

Part III

STRIKING FEAR IN THE HEART OF THE WHITE MAN

2000 – 2001

"Just a Little Row of Trespass..."

In February 2000, the government lost the referendum on its proposed new constitution. A "yes" vote would have entrenched the power of the ruling party, ZANU PF. Recognising this, the people, sick and tired of bad governance, voted "No". They were indicating their disapproval of the ruling party's many excesses and saying "No" to corruption, exploitation, poverty and elitism.

An alternative to the ruling party had appeared on the scene: the MDC (The Movement for Democratic Change). And with the advent of this new party came the pledge of change. The MDC offered hope for the future and promised that, if elected, they as the people's representatives, would be accountable to the electorate.

The nation was swept with a sense of excitement and apprehension. How would the President respond?

In a statesmanlike speech (reminiscent of his impressive Independence Speech in 1980), President Mugabe announced that the government would respect the will of the people with regard to the "No" vote. In fact, he intended nothing of the sort. The government realised that it had miscalculated. The June election was not going to be the walkover it had expected. For the first time since independence twenty years before, it would actually have to *fight* an election.

One can accuse ZANU PF politicians of corruption, extortion and amoral behaviour. But one can never say that they are unintelligent and slow to act or react. They are diabolically clever. When they have their backs to the wall, they fight with every weapon and trick at their disposal. Which was exactly what they did. They regrouped and attacked immediately with a fiendish plan of action. They knew that they had to retain power, no matter what the cost. If they failed to do so, they would lose everything and many members of the hierarchy would find themselves in jail, some possibly facing the death sentence for crimes against humanity.

The Catholic Commission for Justice and Peace in Zimbabwe and the Legal Resources Foundation had researched and documented the suffering of the people of Matabeleland and the Midlands and the human rights abuses perpetrated during the Gukurahundi. Their report "Breaking the Silence, Building True Peace" had been released in 1997. They commented that most people in Zimbabwe (other than those actually living in the affected areas) had little idea of what the Gukurahundi was like and of how people still suffered as a result of the violence that had taken place. "We need the truth of what happened to be revealed," the report stated, "so that reconciliation can begin."

The brief period of stability and national unity had come to an end.

Mugabe and his ZANU PF colleagues had decided to use their trump card: to focus on the emotive issue of the land. This would resonate throughout Africa and ensure they had the crucial backing of African governments.

Within days, the farm invasions began. White farms were invaded, farmers attacked and black farm workers victimised, intimidated and brutally assaulted. So-called "War Veterans", many in their late teens or early twenties, and far too young to have fought in the liberation struggle, were hired by the government to occupy the farms and prevent the farmers and their employees from working. Their mandate was also to "re-educate" the rural people so that they would be sure to vote ZANU PF in the June election. The occupied farms were to be "redistributed" to blacks, who would take them over and continue the work of farming. In fact, very little of the appropriated land was given to genuine farmers and the main beneficiaries were, in the best traditions of the ZANU PF patronage system, its own dignitaries and their cronies.

The systematic terror campaign waged against white farmers and their black farm workers immediately hit the headlines. Horrifying pictures of jeering armed mobs breaking into homesteads and farm villages, and setting houses, tobacco barns, crops, clinics and schools alight were shown on BBC, CNN and Sky News. Photographs of brutally beaten and tortured farmers, their wives and their workers appalled viewers throughout the civilised world. The mobs, like swarms of voracious locusts, looted and laid waste everything in their paths.

In the towns and cities, we urban dwellers trembled with dismay and apprehension at the outrage. It seemed that, apart from praying for the farmers' safety, there was nothing we could do to help or support them, especially those in very remote areas with only one access road blockaded by hostile police. It was terrible and we all felt traumatised by our inability to assist. But we were amazed and encouraged by their steadfast, courageous behaviour. How did they manage to keep calm in the presence of these drug and drink-crazed weapon-wielding hordes?

I was completely overwhelmed by the horror of what was happening in the rural areas. Coming from farming stock, I knew what it was like to live far from the nearest town and miles away from one's neighbours. In those days, however, the police would have responded immediately to a call for help. The situation, now, was very different. The police and the army had been instructed by the ruling party to *participate* in the farm invasions and to *assist* the "so called" war vets. The only help would come from neighbouring farmers, who were themselves in danger.

In despair, I withdrew, as always, to the solace of reading. My sister had given me a book for Christmas called "The Artist's Way" by Julia Cameron. The lessons this book taught became my lifeline during the dark days and often sleepless nights. My journey of self-discovery could not have come at a better time. I learned to cope and to be positive in what was a frightening and negative environment. I learned to feel less guilty about everything imaginable and to be active rather than passive and depressed.

One of the "tools" Julia Cameron advocated was "Morning Pages". This entailed doing three pages first thing each morning in one's own handwriting, strictly stream-of-consciousness. It meant getting up an hour earlier (even in winter). You wrote down whatever came into your head, whether it was a whinge or whine of self-pity, a description of the cat purring on your lap or how you longed to be a successful author.

Julia talked about a sense of possibility. Her contention was that we were all "artists", creative beings that needed to be awakened. We should stop telling ourselves that it was "too late". Or that we would fail. She also declared that we should stop taking life too seriously. Everyone deserved "time out". We should nurture ourselves and learn "to play", to be joyful and to have fun.

So while our rural world was crumbling, I was trying to discover a way of maintaining some sense of equilibrium that would enable me to work and interact "normally" and positively. Everyone was battling with the shocking realisation that the rule of law no longer applied in Zimbabwe. The forces of "law and order" were waging war on their fellow citizens, the very people they had sworn to protect. The feeling of helplessness that we all experienced living in a country spinning out of control was exhausting and debilitating.

I started writing my Morning Pages.

14 April

Paradoxically, the whites and blacks have become closer. With the emergence of the MDC, we have encountered a new breed of politicians. Professor Welshman Ncube and his colleagues seem to have a genuine agenda and they are eager that we all work together.

Everyone is concerned about the safety and the welfare of the rural people. Traditionally, the farmers have cared for their own workers. They've built them schools and given them medical care. Now the rural folk are pawns and important politically.

15 April

This must be the most difficult period our country has experienced. It is impossible to rest easily when our farmers are in such danger and themselves unable to sleep. HOW can we help them? There is serious trouble brewing in the Virginia-

Macheke district east of Harare according to reports from the BBC. We hear that more than 1,000 farms throughout the country have been occupied. It's difficult to know what is going on, since we can't rely on ZTV to report anything accurately.

16 April

Yesterday was a nightmare. David Stevens, a white farmer and a key member of the MDC in the area, has been killed. We hear that he sought refuge at Murehwa Police Station. It seems that the police simply stood and watched as he was seized by a mob of armed squatters, who took him away from the police station, beat him viciously and then executed him. His black foreman, Julius Andoche, was also murdered. Five other white farmers, who had gone to his assistance, were badly beaten. All had to be hospitalised. It's hard to imagine how they will ever recover from their injuries. Farmers and their families in the area have been advised by the Commercial Farmers' Union to evacuate their farms until there's a return to the rule of law.

What it would be like to live in a country like Ireland, where you wake up every morning to a sense of stability and security? Where you don't have to wonder whether tomorrow you will still have a business left? Where, in The Republic, there is a sense of continuity and permanence. We have Irish passports if all else fails, thank God.

19 April

Another farmer, Martin Olds, has been killed. This time from our part of the country - Nyamandhlovu.

Kofi Annan has appealed to President Mugabe to defuse the situation. Will they listen to him because he is black? Do they view him as a 'brother'?

Representatives of the white farmers met with Mugabe on Friday and Saturday and he promised them that he would give the situation his personal attention. Then, yesterday, during his independence message to the nation, he blamed the terrible unrest in the country on them. He referred to them as "our enemies".

Stephen, a black friend, says the rural people see through Mugabe. I hope he's right. If he's wrong, our business will fold, and all our employees will be out of work. People will leave in droves.

20 April

Only the cats are stirring. Ambrose is grooming himself and Mission is on my knee, as usual.

None of us can sleep properly these days. Nothing even approaches normality.

Shakespeare said:

"...Each new morn,
New widows howl, new orphans cry; new sorrows
Strike heaven on the face...."

Although he was talking of Scotland, he could have been referring to Zimbabwe.

21 April

Another farm burned yesterday and many farm workers' homes were torched. Two women were gang-raped. Apart from the dreadful physical and psychological trauma, their exposure to AIDS is a very real possibility. We have to be informed, but feel consumed by anger, loathing and frustration when watching and listening to news bulletins. I can't bear to watch Chenjerai "Hitler" Hunzvi parading about with his cell phone. He uses it as a prop to block out reporters and to look important. It's hard to believe that this brute, who has rocketed to political prominence and power as Chairman of the War Veterans' Association, practises as a doctor of medicine.

I walk outside to look at the sky. There are rows of little delicate pinkish clouds that are now gradually turning orange in the east. The air is crisp and fresh. The trees and shrubs are becoming greener, brighter and more defined. A few minutes ago, they were dark silhouettes. It's going to be a beautiful day.

22 April

Sean's birthday. He's 28 today. I wish he were here with us and not in Australia. And not with that girl who has such a high opinion of herself. I don't think he'll be there much longer, though. Their relationship doesn't seem to be working out, if his letters are anything to go by. We'd certainly love to have him back at Alfa.

The old pine tree outside the window is wet through after yesterday's storm and now the first rays of the sun are warming it. Steam billows off the bark, as if its branches are being ironed.

I must keep busy. Inaction makes me think too much.

Thinking too much makes me desperate.

26 April

It must be awful for my sister to talk to me on the phone these days. My problem is that I've got to keep tight control the whole time, because all I want to do is cry. Weep for the things that are happening here. Howl and sob because people are being intimidated and are dying. Bash my head against the wall when I think that our business might collapse. Shriek with rage when I see pictures of beaten people, injured animals and barns with tobacco in them set alight. We feel impotent, hamstrung, confined, in bondage. And there is nothing we can do to help.

We can pray, Glyn says.

28 April

We talked last night about what we thought would happen to our company. Larry feels it might bleed to death through a process of attrition. People do not *have to have* calendars, diaries and business gifts. Promotional items are not essential. If orders don't start coming in very soon, we'll simply be paying out and paying out, our overdraft facility will probably be withdrawn and we'll just have to close down.

It will be difficult conducting our monthly meeting. The reps need to understand the situation without being panicked.

It will take a large measure of tact and diplomacy to handle this, I reckon. Larry seems to rule out racial violence directed against individuals in the towns at this stage. I am not so sure. If criminal elements get out of hand and think they have carte blanche to behave as they wish – then anything can happen....

1 May

Sometimes people *can* help.

A farmer's wife in the Macheke-Marondera district was visiting her mother-in-law on a neighbouring farm. Intruders broke into the house and bound and gagged the two women. They had guns, but there was no shooting until her husband came to collect her. He was shot in the spleen. The wound bled profusely and his condition became critical. When the word got out on the grape-vine that blood was needed, so many potential donors raced to assist, that the queue outside the hospital stretched round the corner into the street...

I have this huge mental block about going to church at the moment. I don't hate God. I don't love Him either. Julia Cameron writes in "The Artist's Way" that God is everywhere and that we can communicate with Him anywhere and at any level. I certainly like that argument: it is valid up to a point and it suits me. If I truly believed this, I wouldn't feel incessantly guilty. I know that if I went to church, I mightn't feel much more enlightened, but I certainly would feel a lot less derelict.

She encourages us to examine our reading habits. I've long realised that I immerse myself in words in the same way that I lie in a hot bath for ages – to escape. I've always referred to "good escapist reads" in book reviews. She advises us to avoid reading for a week.

5 May

I think she is right that reading voraciously can be like alcohol abuse. It can blot out other things and can leave one, in many ways, frustrated, impoverished and one-dimensional. Since I've always believed that reading is invariably beneficial, this is certainly something of a paradox.

So I've done other things that make me feel I've achieved more, like getting to know my new sewing machine, cooking, cleaning and tidying. We watched "Sixth Sense" which was excellent. I haven't wasted the entire weekend gobbling up a book or books. This is called "recovery". You have to get to like yourself, enjoy your own company (I thought I did) and learn to be more open-minded.

And for my "time out" I lay in a hot bubble bath for an hour with scented candles burning on the window sills and listened to Neil Diamond.

7 May

Book Club yesterday was traumatic. After the reviews we were talking about candlelight protest marches, church services and political meetings. Colleen said that it was a whole load of crap, as none of it would do any good, and she was sick and tired of trying to make things work. Destructive energy was sparking out of her. She was like a grenade about to detonate.

I took her outside, and, after a while, was able to calm her. The poor girl just cried and cried. I think this was the release she needed from all the churning resentment and impotent rage she'd been experiencing. We realised that she'd been bottling her distress for some time and that we all needed to be more sensitive to one another's problems and concerns, and not so caught up in our own.

9 May

Another farmer has been killed. This was after a calculated vicious beating that took place in broad daylight. Like the others, Alan Dunn was an MDC activist. He died in hospital yesterday, God rest his soul. The farmers have continued to behave with great courage, restraint and dignity. The murder of another of their number must be a dreadful blow to their morale.

I've been thinking about what happened at Book Club.

Colleen is watching her adopted country crashing down about her, and there is nothing she can do to stop the process.

She is seeing her son's career and business ventures threatened with ruin. She and Liam came out to this country to escape the discrimination they had faced in Northern Ireland. Now there is a vicious pogrom in place in Zimbabwe targeting the whites. No wonder she's bitter.

HONEYMOON DESTINATION

As we turned off down the dirt road to Malalangwe Lodge, Alex became even more excited. "I do not want to see snakes or spiders," he confessed. "I am very much afraid of these. But I would love to see a lion." We told him that there were no lions in this area, but that we were likely to see wildebeest, zebra, giraffe, warthog and many different kinds of antelope. We would be unlikely to see leopard, even though the Matobo Hills have the largest leopard population in the world. Casual visitors rarely saw them, we explained, since they were nocturnal animals.

Alex's company in Spain supplied us with pens. This was his first visit to Zimbabwe, and we'd decided to take him out to Malalangwe, one of our favourite places. Larry and I hadn't had a weekend away from town in ages, so this would be a treat for us, too.

We wound slowly down the road, scanning the bush on either side for game. Alex was fascinated by the bush itself and by the bird life. As we rounded each bend, we experienced a tingling sense of anticipation. We saw a distant herd of impala and two or three zebra closer to the road. It was great fun having an enthusiastic guest with us, someone who wanted to linger and gaze and appreciate. He was not the sort of tourist who insisted on seeing everything second-hand through the lens of a video camera.

Not long afterwards, we were sitting in the lounge at the lodge, sipping cold beers and chatting with our hosts about how things were in these difficult times. They were finding that they were now mainly reliant on the local market, since very few foreigners were visiting the country. All their other guests that weekend were locals, so our Spaniard was positively exotic.

Alex wandered about, examining the sculptures, carvings and woven baskets that decorated the room. He gently stroked the back of a wooden giraffe and commented that he hoped he would see "this animal". A moment later, three stately adult giraffe walked unhurriedly past the lodge. Alex could hardly believe his eyes. It was as if they had been waiting obediently in the wings for their cue.

Late in the afternoon we went on a leisurely game drive. Tendai, our guide and driver, stopped each time there was anything interesting to discuss. He explained that the closest relative to the little dassies[7] darting about among the rocks was, incongruously, the elephant. The clear, sharp whistle some distance away was the Boulder Chat, while the cheerful "chit, chit, chit" sounds closer to us, were two Black-eyed Bulbuls. At one point he stopped the truck and led us through the tall grass to a nest hidden among some exposed tree roots. Gently he moved the grass aside and indicated a single bright blue egg that looked just like the beautifully painted Easter eggs in my recipe books. He had found it the previous day while out on patrol.

Tendai told us that he and the other scouts patrolled each day recording data relating to flora and fauna on the farm. Each person had his own sector to cover. He was required to note such information as movements of animals from one area to another, what they ate, their groupings and their condition. Rainfall was recorded and comparisons made between one year and another. Different species of trees were very important to the ecology of the area and their development was charted.

Of great concern, Tendai explained, was the problem of tick infestation. There were very few oxpeckers in the area, since some farmers had been using DDT insecticides on their crops. So, lacking the assistance of the birds, the animals had to be protected by artificial means in order to control the scourge of ticks. He showed us a series of enclosures fashioned from branches where large blocks of salt had been placed. The animals were lured into these "bomas" by the promise of salt "licks", which they loved. As they walked through the entrance of the boma to approach the salt, they depressed a concealed trigger, activating an insecticide spray.

---

7 Rock hyraxes

"Take us to the place where the leopard passes," we urged Tendai, as the light began to fade. Perhaps, *this* evening, we might actually see one. It would certainly be the highlight of Alex's trip to Africa.

Tendai drove slowly up the narrow track between the rugged kopjes[8]. Even the chirping of the crickets was suspended here. As the night closed in, we examined each bush and thicket, and craned our necks to search the trees above us, in case a leopard was stretched out on a branch, looking down disdainfully.

Nothing moved.

But that did not mean there was nothing there.

It was a relief to leave this claustrophobic place and to move beyond it to the open vlei[9], where the moon rode proudly and the star-studded sky stretched free above us. In the distance the lights of the lodge beckoned us to hot baths, drinks and dinner.

At sunrise the next morning we left the lodge to go for a walk. How different from being in town, when you drag yourself from the clutches of sleep in response to the strident shriek of your bedside clock or the insistent whirring vibration of your cell phone's alarm. We didn't talk much at first. Each person was wrapped in his or her own thoughts. It was a time to savour the sound of birds indulging in lively repartee. Our destination was a kopje where there were spectacular rock paintings. Tendai pointed out the spoor of several eland that had been browsing recently in the area. Branches had been pulled down at random, and he commented that only a limited number of eland could be sustained in a given area, as they ruined the vegetation.

We left the trail and climbed a sloping granite outcrop to admire the view. All around us were kopjes of different shapes and sizes, and trees and grassland stretched as far as the eye could see. From this vantage point we marvelled at the many shades of green, the sharply defined rock formations and the

---

8 Kopje: a small isolated hill. (Afrikaans – a little head.)
9 Vlei: an area of low marshy ground in which water collects during the rainy season.

"living blue" of the sky. Tiny toy animals, far away, grazed peacefully in the dewy veldt.

We wandered back down to the trail. Alex found Tendai extremely interesting, particularly as our guide knew the Latin names of all the bushes and trees found on the farm. Spanish did, after all, "come from" Latin, Alex reminded us. Tendai took us off the main trail to the kopje where some particularly interesting bushman paintings were. He explained that scholars had different theories as to what exactly the illustrations depicted. The paintings of animals were usually obvious, but the human figures were often more ambiguous. What were these people doing? It was fascinating to speculate. Some seemed to be in a trance-like state, others were hunting. Hyrax urine had unfortunately obscured a small section of the painting at this site. This was such a pity, as most of the artwork was still clear with the figures painted in a strong reddish-brown.

We realised that we were hungry and thirsty and that the sun was much hotter. Bacon, sausages and eggs followed by a swim seemed like a good idea.

"I would like to come to Zimbabwe for my honeymoon," Alex announced as we drove back to Bulawayo.

We were delighted. Perhaps we would become a tourist destination for the people of Barcelona?

"I just have to meet the right girl," said Alex frowning.

"Greater Law and Order..."

15 May
The death of a fourth farmer has made everyone even more jittery. Yet, somehow, this death is not as shocking as the deaths of the others. I think the difference is that violence is no longer a new phenomenon. We've been trying to come to terms with the collapse of law and order for more than three months. I don't think people can cope with living at a fever pitch of horror and desolation indefinitely.

19 May
The sun is shining, but it's cold and windy. Perhaps the war vets won't be quite so eager to assert themselves if they're shivering and uncomfortable. Imagine how frustrating it must be for the farmers. These war vets, many of them the dregs of the cities, have been planted on the farms to intimidate their employees. Crops cannot be reaped and these ruffians actually have the gall to demand food, shelter and transport. One moment they're burning your tobacco crop and the next they're asking for a lift to town. It's insane.

There has been only the barest mention on the international news of John Weeks, the fourth farmer to die four days after being shot in the chest. Journalists have moved on to cover the dreadful fireworks explosion in the Netherlands.

I am fascinated by Julia Cameron's assertion that the creative process is about "getting something down" as opposed to "thinking something up". In other words, discipline rather than inspiration.

22 May
Shirley's kittens are so cute. I would love to have the ginger one. It's a downy, marmalade ball. Unlike its two little grey and black sisters, it seems to be unafraid and full of vitality. I wonder whether I can talk Larry into our taking it.

I am excited as I'm going to proof-read Mike Lipkin's latest book with Glyn. I've never done anything like this before, and I'm sure it'll be a wonderful experience. Mike Lipkin is a motivational speaker who divides his time between Canada and South Africa. Larry and I attended a lecture of his on selling techniques in Durban several years ago. He had us jumping to our feet, punching our fists in the air and fervently shouting, "Yes! Yes! Yes!" It was rather like being at an evangelical gathering, where the preacher has his audience declaring they're "re-born".

28 May

The month of June will be gruelling. There's going to be a four-week run-up to the elections. Re-education (or the systematic intimidation and brainwashing) of the rural people is being carried out by the ZANU PF machine. They must be using "Nineteen Eighty-Four" as their textbook. "Freedom is slavery" springs to mind.

The war veterans round up farm workers (having burned down their homes, raped their women and beaten them) and march them to indoctrination sessions, which sometimes last for days. They have to sing liberation songs, punch the air with their fists and chant ZANU PF slogans. Suspected MDC supporters are singled out and beaten some more.

1 June

Last night we were invited to Stella and Terry's house to listen to Dave Coltart. We've been asked to design and print leaflets for the MDC and are working with Stella and Terry on the project. It was a very small gathering, so we were able to ask as many questions as we liked. Dave is essentially a human rights activist, rather than a politician.

He said that he was disturbed to hear that large numbers of whites were planning to leave the country to "go on holiday" before the elections. He urged everyone to vote and to go "on holiday" afterwards.

Glyn's couriered parcel arrived safely. Mike Lipkin's book is called "Juiced!" Sounds like him! I'm really looking forward to working on it. We certainly need motivation and encouragement in this neck of the woods.

15 June

The countdown period is truly unnerving. We just want to get the elections over so that we can take up our lives again and move beyond this eerie state of limbo. The situation saps our strength and courage, as the constant "what if?" questions bombard us. What can it be like on the farms?

Olly is the most delightful kitten. He's a never-still ball of orange fluff, extremely mischievous and very affectionate.

Some good things have been happening. Sean is happier in Oz now that he and Sally have parted. Brian and his girl friend Robin have moved to a lovely house - they are no longer in that horrible, dark place with too much long grass and too many bad vibes. And there was a beautiful rainbow on Friday.

Mike Lipkin was pleased with our efforts, and paid Glyn an extra R1,000 for our proof-reading. This is how he defines the term "juiced": "...filled with power, vitality, commitment, energy; really turned on and fired up; unstoppable and irresistible". "Juiced!" is about succeeding in business through "spectacular customer service". One of his mantras is: "Live large; play big; finish strong". The man is a dynamo. I learned a lot and enjoyed the exercise, particularly since it took my mind off Zim. I'll put "Juiced!" into Book Club when Glyn sends me a copy. The girls have enjoyed some of his other books. Marilyn attended one of his seminars for directors' wives on a house boat on Kariba. Very civilised.

16 June

I felt exhausted yesterday after making a sincere effort at work to be positive, encouraging and "juiced". Our Leader continues to spout his rhetoric everywhere he goes, and while it doesn't convert people, it does depress them. The MDC's campaign is hotting up, too, and we are working on three lots of information leaflets at the moment. (It's illegal, of course, to print "subversive matter" so we have to be very careful.)

Stella is such a good person. She is totally sincere, and has channelled all her energy into working for the MDC. She and Terry run around all day long to assist Dave. She looks worn out much of the time, poor darling.

17 June

This time next week it will be Election Day. We are all sick and tired of the tension, fear and uncertainty. We are all sick and tired of the violence.

Our Beloved Leader is in town today to preside at a rally. All of a sudden, fuel is available and there are no queues. Amazing.

We, in the towns, do not know how the rural people are going to vote. From the stories we hear (mostly government-inspired) they have been cowed into submission. They are not going to vote at all or they are going to vote for the ruling party. And what about the farm workers who have been so viciously brutalised, their women raped and their houses burnt to the ground? How will *they* vote? *Will* they vote? Have they been totally intimidated, or will they be bravely angry and eager for their moment in the polling booth to take their sweet revenge?

Is there any hope? I think there is. After twenty years there is a genuine opposition party in this country. Although its leaders do not pretend to know all the answers, they appear to be men of principle, who genuinely seem to care about the ordinary people like us.

They've been working tirelessly to get their message across in spite of being denied access to the government-run daily newspapers, radio and television. We are made aware of meetings and rallies by word of mouth or through email.

Our people are suffering and we are angry. Collectively angry. Please God that our anger will be brought to the ballot boxes when we cast our votes in a week's time.

21 June

It's Brian's 26th birthday today. I hope that it will be a happy day for him. It's certainly an auspicious time to have a birthday.

The MDC is becoming more confident by the day. At first they were talking about "if" we win. Now they are talking about "when". There seems little doubt as to how urban people are going to vote. MDC meetings have been incredibly well attended. This has not been the case with ZANU PF rallies.

We've been told that the ruling party is putting every obstacle possible in the way of the opposition. Stella says you need a degree to be an election monitor, the instructions are so complicated. I just hope that we can pull it off.

24 June: Election Day 1

Well, for better or worse, it's Election Day. We believe that there IS a very real chance that the MDC will win in spite of all the attempts at rigging that we've been warned about, and all the dirty tricks. The ruling party must be worried. I just hope that worry doesn't translate into more violence. There are rumours that the youth militia is being bussed into town.

Let the voice of the people be heard and let it be a righteous voice that cries out for justice and for CHANGE.

25 June: Election Day 2.

Charles arrived early yesterday to drive our truck up to the MDC Command Centre. Whites would be glaringly obvious cruising around the western suburbs. At 8:30 am Larry and I met Brian and Robin at Ascot, where there were long queues. It took us more than two hours to vote. While we were there, the clouds gradually came over and the sun disappeared. It got colder and colder and we all shivered, stamped our feet and jumped about trying to get warm. Everyone was in good spirits, though, in spite of the cold. I'm sure we'll find that there has been a record turnout, especially in the urban constituencies.

Stella called us at lunchtime and we went to their house to man the radio in case they needed to call for back up, as they were patrolling the western reaches of Dave's constituency as far as Nketa. Although we're not in the front line, it's a relief to be able to do something to help.

Charles got back very late last night. He must have been exhausted, but he's always cheerful. He'd had an interesting day. He "escorted" the official truck carrying the ballot boxes to the place where they were to be locked up and guarded for the night. Originally this was to be Donnington Police Station, but I have an idea they landed up at Nketa School. MDC personnel were present and watching for ballot box stuffing.

Apparently counting will start tonight at 8 pm I've got an awful hollow feeling in my stomach. I don't know whether it's nerves, indigestion or both.

It's impossible to think of anything else today. I wasn't even upset that England beat the Springboks in the second test. The Boks had a few good phases, but the game was very scrappy and they never looked as if they'd get it together.

26 June

Elections are over and the votes are to be counted today. It has been a long, but far from relaxing weekend. We will all go to work tired and nervous, and spend the day listening to the radio.

28 June

I couldn't face writing my pages yesterday with the election scenario unfolding.

We were devastated about the results, as we had come to believe that the MDC would have a landslide victory. The final results are ZANU PF 62, MDC 57 and Independents 1. While this sounds great, we must not forget that the President will be appointing 30 of his own people (as well as the 62 "elected") to parliament to "serve" the nation. Nonetheless, we will now have a truly effective opposition, which will be able to block any further changes to the constitution. We had, of course, hoped for a new government. The MDC is apparently planning to challenge 20 seats.

Yesterday was a truly awful day. I felt desperate, unsettled and confused. There are so many "What ifs?"

I am the hostess for our July Book Club. I'll probably buy a cheesecake and sausage rolls and make sandwiches and a quiche. I don't have the energy to do much elaborate baking. I hope that Colleen will be feeling less depressed and unhappy. When I phoned her after Diana's Book Club, she sounded better – more calm and controlled.

I'm worried about Stella. I haven't seen her this week. She and Terry put their lives on hold for months to work for the MDC. How do they feel at the moment? Are they despondent or encouraged by the fact that the opposition did so well in the towns and cities? They must be delighted and relieved, though, that Dave won Bulawayo South by such a large margin of votes.

30 July

My pages are irregular these days, mainly because of the cold, which tends to put my mind in neutral. I can't imagine what it must be like to live in a cold country like Canada. How do they ever get anything done? I would want to go into hibernation for the duration of winter. I suppose their homes are heated, which would make a considerable difference. I miss "The Artist's Way" now that I've finished reading it.

I'm going to enrol for a computer course, something I've been meaning to do for ages. I need to cultivate Mike Lipkin's "opportunity consciousness".

We keep hearing rumours about more farmers being killed.

1 August

The MDC called for a stay-away from work yesterday. We must have been the only place in the town centre that closed in response to their call. Larry told our factory workers not to report for work. It was frustrating, especially since sales have just begun to pick up, and there is a lot of printing to do. Stay-aways are utterly pointless if businesses ignore the MDC's request and continue to operate as normal. And now the MDC is talking about a three-day stay-away at the end of the week. As Larry says, these must be well-organised if they are to work. I know it is very difficult for the MDC, as they have to operate almost entirely by word of mouth, being denied access to radio, television and government-run newspapers, but vagueness and lack of decisive leadership will do their cause no good.

Parliament opens today after all sorts of delaying tactics by the ruling party. The MDC should, finally, be able to use its voice to condemn the government for its criminal behaviour and its many excesses. Dave says that the process of change has begun, and that, no matter what happens in the next few months, in the long term, Zimbabwe will never be the same again.

We're going to Malalangwe for the weekend. I can't wait. We haven't been out to the lodge since we took Alex there. I'll always remember his delight when he saw those three giraffe.

13 August

Sunday morning in the Matobo Hills. Everything is tranquil. Starlings are perched on the aloes near our balcony. In the distance a dove is calling. As we walked in the veldt yesterday, lines of poetry and snippets of prose danced through my head, and I longed to fasten onto them and make them materialise on the page. I wanted to try to capture the essence of the bush: the sense of wonder and the feeling of closeness to God and to creation that is seldom present in a town.

The bush in winter has a beauty of its own. The tall, brown grass rustles and whispers as we pass through it and then quietly resumes its original position, as if we were never there.

28 September

As things get busier at work, I'm finding it more and more difficult to write my pages regularly. We're already working shifts at Alfa, which means that Sean, Larry and I get home after 10 pm during the week. It's great having Sean back. He's planning to do an MBA through Rhodes University next year.

We were talking to Greg yesterday about Hwange Game Reserve. He's chairman of the Matabeleland Branch of the Wildlife Society of Zimbabwe. He's very concerned about the effect of the "land distribution programme" on wildlife in the park. Poaching is reaching epidemic proportions, and he's worried about the rhino, in particular. Animals are being snared and left to rot. Some have had their tendons cut or their entrails pulled out. It's brutal and malicious. He tells us that trees in the park are being chopped down and sold. He knows government ministers are involved.

8 October

We're all very subdued at Book Club these days. Everyone is exhausted. The most popular books are detective stories and thrillers. Anything to escape. Michael Connelly, P.D. James, Minette Walters, Kathy Reichs – we can't get enough of them. We've decided to have our Christmas lunch this year at The Castle. It's so beautiful there, and, if it doesn't rain, we can sit by the pool.

25 October

Yesterday we saw a report on our tourist industry compiled by the Zimbabwe Tourism Authority. The year to date has been a disaster. Businesses are closing and workers are being retrenched. Foreign tourists have cancelled bookings. They would rather visit countries where the rule of law applies. Fuel shortages have affected the domestic and South African markets.

The tourist industry had been one of the fastest-growing economic sectors in the country.

30 November

Each day we battle to get the jobs out before shutdown in three weeks' time. The unrealistic demands exhaust us. We have to fight fires from every angle. People who ordered two weeks ago are wondering where their orders are! It's difficult not to shriek with hysterical laughter sometimes.

It's Book Club on Saturday and I'm looking forward to a relaxing morning in female company.

15 December

My whole life revolves around diaries at the moment. I can't sleep. The outstanding jobs parade through my head all night.

21 December

Glyn and Ian arrive from South Africa tomorrow.

Today is our last day at work before we shut down for the Christmas and New Year break. What bliss. No more frantic efforts to get deliveries out. No more irate telephone calls. Poor Gillian has had a hellish time in Harare, with the chronic fuel shortage. Yet she has managed to get all our deliveries done and has organised the foiling of personalisations on most of the remaining diary orders.

The factory has performed extremely well. Our despatch department has been fantastic and the team tasked with tipping title pages into the diaries has done an excellent job. Everyone is tired and needs this break.

Somehow we have got through this terrible year.

19 September 2001

Yesterday we launched our book "Voices of Zimbabwe" at Walkers in Bulawayo. Everyone from Book Club was there to support us.

Larry, Glyn and I decided in January that we were going to do something constructive. Last year we were forced to watch terrible things happen. We decided that we weren't going to sit by as observers for another year, watching ZANU's game-plan for 2001 unfold. We were going to write a book that would present a balanced picture of what was happening to our country. Perhaps we could make a difference. We would have ordinary people speak out: the farm workers; the farmers under siege; the journalists imprisoned for reporting the truth; even the war "veterans" – the vicious brutes, who are malleable puppets of the Party.

We've had an exciting six months. Every spare moment has gone into the research and the writing of "Voices". I've missed a number of Book Club meetings, since we've had to do the artwork and origination in the studio on Saturdays. Glyn met many of the farmers we had read about, among them Maria Stevens and Kerry Kay. Maria's husband, David, was the first farmer to be murdered. Kerry's husband, Iain, was with him when this happened. Iain has been attacked twice and savagely beaten on both occasions. They're no longer on their farm. Kerry is Project Manager for the Commercial Farmers' Union AIDS Control Programme. Glyn attended Gloria Olds' funeral where the minister called upon God to curse the murderers of this 72 year old farmer (the mother of Martin who was killed last year). Mrs. Olds had devoted much of her life to helping needy black people. The Rev. Paul Andrianatos was forced to leave the country two days later.

Larry wrote about the land. He explained that many blacks believe arrogant white settlers stole the land from them and have no right to own it. They don't acknowledge the importance of the commercial farming sector to the nation's economy. They don't seem to realise that squatters, who occupy land to which they hold no title, will never be able to use it as security for the raising of working capital. There will be no development without adequate funding – commercial farming will grind to a halt. And subsistence farming generates neither employment nor foreign currency. Robert Mugabe knows this as well as we do, but he has no intention of relinquishing the reins of power. He incites hatred and resentment of the whites to entrench his position, and talks about how the white farmers are suffering "that very little inconvenience".

This is *my* country. Zimbabwe belongs to all of us and it's worth fighting for. I will not embrace apathy and tolerate anarchy and brutality with a shrug and say, "It's not my problem..."

Tonight we fly to Harare to launch "Voices" there.

Part IV

ENEMIES OF THE STATE

2002 – 2004

HEROES

12 August, 2002 (Heroes' Day)

Mr Mugabe must be relieved to have a new hero to honour today. Dr. Bernard Chidzero's death this week will have taken the pressure off him. He can now expound upon the late Minister of Finance's achievements and on his loyalty to Zimbabwe. Then, having extolled the virtues of heroes past (one of the more recent additions being rabid Dr. Hunzvi, who died in June last year), he'll punch his fist in the air and rant at length about matters of concern to the people of Zimbabwe. These are: colonial oppressors (in particular Blair and Bush); the fact that Zimbabwe is not for sale; the perfidious EU and homosexuals and other "perverts". Finally, he'll remind everyone that recurring drought is the cause of our food crisis.

Thousands of ZANU PF supporters bussed to Heroes' Acre will applaud him wildly. They'll be hoping they won't miss out on the free food and beer to be distributed later in the afternoon. Mugabe's cheerleaders - hundreds of obese women - will be leading the songs of praise and the chanting of party slogans. They'll be wearing their usual gear – head scarves and full-length dresses in primary colours. Mr. Mugabe's face will grace the contours of their huge bosoms and massive posteriors.

Most farmers have been ordered to leave their farms. They're enemies of the State. Hundreds of thousands of their workers will be displaced. They'll become wandering vagrants with no homes and no jobs. There'll be no crops, dairy products or meat.

Five months ago, we did everything possible to win the Presidential Election. We thought we'd anticipated every fraudulent move the ZANU PF machine would make. Brave people died. Others were assaulted and tortured, and many lost their homes and belongings. Hundreds of MDC members went into hiding.

We were naïve. Mugabe was "elected" to serve his fourth term, and a few days later, he took the oath of office. I wanted to puke, as I watched him swear to be "faithful" and to "observe" the laws of Zimbabwe.

20 August

Morgan Tsvangirai's trumped-up treason charge is still pending, and he seems to have been silenced for the moment, which is worrying. We're being force-fed anti-white bulletins by the government media who've developed their own version of Oceania's glorious victories and the Two Minutes Hate. Our Emmanuel Goldstein is that "gangster" at Number 10 Downing Street. Soccer is our Victory gin.

There's a story doing the rounds about an elderly Marondera couple who were dragged off to the police station and interrogated for hours.

The police may charge them under the new POSA[10] legislation with having insulted the President and with attempting to engender feelings of hostility towards him. They could go to prison for a year. When Mugabe's motorcade came hurtling through the town with sirens blaring and lights flashing, the old lady turned to her husband and said, "What a waste of fuel."

They're also enemies of the State.

It's impossible for people living elsewhere to imagine the despair and frustration we are feeling. We had hoped that the international community's condemnation of the stolen election and Zimbabwe's suspension from the Commonwealth would have an impact on Mugabe's credibility. But the African states are supporting Mugabe as usual. They're not going to do anything to help us, even though it's obvious that black people are suffering in far greater numbers than white people.

There are queues for maize meal, queues for bread, queues for sugar, queues for salt and queues for cooking oil.

---

10 POSA: Public Order and Security Act

Inflation is going crazy. The current rate of the Zimbabwe dollar to the US dollar is 750 to 1 on the parallel market[11]. Yet, somehow, business goes on.

30 August

The distributors for "Voices of Zimbabwe" in Jo'burg have gone into liquidation. We're not going to realise a cent for any books "sold" in South Africa. Instead we're going to have to convince the Reserve Bank that there have been no proceeds from sales. Larry says we're also likely to have a problem repatriating any unsold books. I wonder whether Cathy Buckle is in the same predicament. She's been using them for "African Tears".

Fortunately, sales here have been very good, and we should cover our printing costs.

4 September

I hate having those 44-gallon drums of petrol and diesel hidden under tarpaulins in the garden.

I'll wake up in the night with my heart pounding. I'll lie there wondering what disturbed me. Dex isn't barking, so it's not someone trying to break in. Then... Crack! It's loud, like a shot being fired. The fuel in those bloody drums is contracting or expanding.

Larry gets irritated when I say how much I loathe having them there. What if they explode and we have a fire, I ask him. I know we have no option, though. We can't keep them at the factory.

---

11 The Parallel Market: The Parallel Market for foreign currency in Zimbabwe is the 'street' or black market, in which foreign currency is bought and sold at a price determined by the normal rules of supply and demand. The seller will sell at the best price he can get and the buyer will pay the minimum he can get away with.

I WANT SOME OF THAT

These days Colleen gets visibly irritated when we go off at tangents during reviews. She doesn't hide her displeasure – she sighs loudly or jumps up to look out of the window. If there's a dog or cat in the room, she's easily distracted, as she loves animals. Sometimes she'll leave the room, ostensibly to help our hostess in the kitchen.

Moira hasn't gone through to the kitchen yet. She's reviewing "The Christmas Tree" by Jennifer Johnston, an Irish author Colleen's introduced us to. Everyone is looking forward to reading it, and I'm hoping that Moira won't reveal the ending.

I find myself watching Colleen nervously. Is she in a confrontational frame of mind today?

Moira is telling us that she and Colin plan to have a family reunion in England this year. She's talking about how she hopes they'll see snow. Now she's picked up "The Christmas Tree" again, and we're back on track.

"Please don't tell us what happens to Constance," I'm thinking.

And I'm watching Colleen.

The fury that often consumed Colleen was exhausting. She'd felt this anger and boiling rage ever since they'd begun to assault and murder the farmers. Farmers who were parents of girls in her classes. Farmers she and Liam knew.

How long had it been since life had been normal? Three years? Four years?

She'd always been dynamic and energetic, throwing herself whole-heartedly into her teaching and drama lessons. She remembered the exhilaration of directing "Grease" several years before. The kids had loved the music and dancing, and had played to full houses every night. Their enthusiasm had been so infectious that their audiences wouldn't let them leave the stage. And the flowers... Being showered with flowers had been intoxicating... It had been stimulating and exciting, although very hard work, involving hours and hours of rehearsals in the evenings and at the weekends. After that it had been "Pride and Prejudice" and after that "The Wind in the Willows"...

For a while she'd been able to escape into the magical worlds inhabited by Danny and Sandy; Darcy and Elizabeth; Mole, Ratty and Mr. Toad.

But only for a while...

Late one evening, several months before, the phone had rung. "I've got cancer," her sister had said. It was less than a year since Jimmy, Brigid's husband had died. Her brother, her mother, Jimmy - all from cancer. And now Brigid, far away in Vermont.

With Liam's blessing, she'd taken a half term's leave and flown over to the States to look after Brigid. In between chemo treatments, the two sisters had travelled to Vancouver Island to visit Brendan. On a lovely sunny May morning, they'd been sitting on a bench in beautiful Butchart Gardens not far from the Blue Poppy Restaurant. Nearby, a group of elderly Canadians, much the same age as Colleen and Brigid, were talking animatedly.

These people were not racing round trying to find petrol.

They were not standing in a bread queue.

They were not clutching their cell phones, handbags and car keys in paranoid fashion.

They were not living behind high walls topped with razor wire.

They were free to say whatever they wanted to say and however loudly they wanted to say it.

These people were relaxed and happy.

"Shit!" Colleen had thought. "*I* want some of that..."

They'd been let down so often by domestic helpers that they wondered whether the frustration of trying to find a suitable person was more trouble than it was worth. Their last domestic worker had decided that she'd do better selling tomatoes at the corner of Cecil Avenue and Nairn Road. She preferred to sit under a tree all day long on the hard, bare earth with her legs stuck out stiffly in front of her. A heap of ripe tomatoes would be piled in a pyramid nearby. Colleen had observed her gossiping with folk strolling past, making little effort to sell her wares. She appeared quite content. The fact that there was no regular income didn't seem to be a problem.

Colleen hated the chores that she would have to come home to. Their house was too big for them. It had been fine when their boys were growing up. But now five bedrooms were excessive. They'd shut off the one wing of the house, to all intents and purposes, and she unlocked this section only intermittently to sweep and dust. She would find herself sitting on the beds in the boys' rooms, staring at photographs of rugby, hockey and water polo teams and wondering where the years had gone.

Moira was chattering on about Christmas lights in small English towns. She was wearing one of those low-cut dresses that showed off her cleavage. Her skirt was far too short. She must be long past fifty, for God's sake. And her hair was too long. And she still hadn't got to the blue lights on Constance's tree.

Colleen wished she'd brought her embroidery. She was restless and edgy. She felt like going outside onto the veranda, but Moira's little Fox Terrier had wound himself round her feet and she didn't want to disturb him.

Their two beautiful Rhodesian Ridgebacks had grown old and died some years before, and their feisty little Bull Terrier had recently died, too. The loss of each had been traumatic. She continued to help with fund-raising for the SPCA and had started an SPCA club at school. These days many animals were in trouble, as people were leaving in droves. The worst time, though, had been two years earlier during the height of the farm invasions, especially in Chinhoyi and Karoi. Courageous people, many of them townsfolk, had braved war veterans to rescue injured and starving animals. Some dogs, cats and horses had been relocated, but there were never enough homes and the old and frail had had to be humanely "put down".

Paul and Felicity had lost their safari operation in the Chinhoyi area when things had fallen apart in August 2001. But they'd moved to Harare, and had started a new business that was already doing very well. They were young and full of plans, confidence and enthusiasm. And they had a beautiful little boy. If she and Liam had reason to hope for a better future, it was because of this beloved grandchild.

Brendan had found a job in Canada easily. Their younger son was such a bright lad. Although he had missed Zim, at first, he was now settled and doing very well. There couldn't be too many agronomists left in Zim, thanks to Mugabe.

Book Club had been a joy for many years, but now she was finding it difficult to summon up enthusiasm even for this. Many of the ladies in the group seemed hopeful and buoyant, in spite of the mess the country was in. Ridiculously so, she often thought. How could they possibly believe that things could come right? It was obvious that the government would never allow the MDC to win an election. What was the point of spending time, money and energy on a lost cause?

She thought about that Book Club meeting when she'd freaked out. The ladies had been talking about church services for torture victims and about political rallies. She'd exploded, overwhelmed by the futility of it all. Why was everyone so blind? Life in Zimbabwe was hellish. It was fine, she supposed, for people who had money outside the country. Like Moira and Jeanette. And probably Marilyn. They could hedge their bets. She and Liam had no external funds. They could return to Ireland, but would they be eligible for pensions and medical care?

They'd left Belfast on their wedding day in 1963 and had invested everything in Rhodesia. But their adopted country was sliding rapidly back towards the dark ages. Their house was too big (she'd loved it so much once). It had become impossibly expensive to maintain and was now a millstone around their necks.

But, no matter what happened, she and Liam had resolved that they would never be a burden to their sons. She sighed and the Fox Terrier lying on her feet opened his eyes and yawned.

Moira was finishing her review.

Colleen's eyes were closed. Was she asleep?

"I loved 'The Christmas Tree'," Moira was saying. "Constance dies on Christmas day, after Jacob Weinberg has arrived to claim his baby daughter. Yet it's not a sad story. The baby is a promise of hope and joy."

Colleen's eyes snapped open.

Was she going to say something provocative?

She shook her head slightly, smiled at me and patted the little dog.

BEIRA

Gillian gave a watery smile and laughed sadly. "There are many wonderful memories. I'll always be grateful for my life in this country, first as Rhodesia and then as Zimbabwe. And I'll never forget those magical holidays in Beira[12]. We had a marvellous time, didn't we? But I believe that we've reached the end of an era. Whites no longer have a place here. Whether you were born here or not makes not the least bit of difference. The blacks must just get on with it. If they are prepared to allow this horrendous situation to continue, well...so be it."

"My nieces and nephews have all gone. Like so many other young people, they are trying to rebuild their lives elsewhere. I'm about to become a statistic in the new exodus, the emigration of people of our age group, who are leaving, not because we want to, but because we have to. No spirit of adventure moves the likes of us. The surrender of my life in Zimbabwe completely traumatises me. Arthur, born and bred here like me, no longer has a valid travel document. You know how difficult it is for a white person to get a Zimbabwean passport renewed. And the silly man has done nothing. If I wait until he gets off his butt, there'll be no escape. I have to get my mother to a place where decent medical attention is available, and where I can afford to pay for the medicines she needs. Ironically, she doesn't want to leave, and they've ganged up and accuse me of being selfish."

She sobbed quietly for a while, and lit another cigarette. Wracked with emotion and too many cigarettes, her voice had become more throaty than usual. I felt like crying myself. I had always admired Gillian's strength of character, courage and confidence. There was little I could say, however, that would comfort her. I could only listen and offer her sympathy and understanding.

---

12 Beira is the second-largest city in Mozambique. It was established in 1890 by the Portuguese. Mozambique originally was the Portuguese-administered territory of Portuguese East Africa.

"I cannot abide the thought of becoming a pensioner in Zimbabwe, dependent on my relatives or on strangers' charity. Someone I know who was a headmaster of one of the most prestigious schools in Harare is almost a pauper. Our pensioners do not deserve such a fate after their investment of time, effort and energy in this country."

She took off her glasses and dried her eyes. "I have no option," she said. "I have to go. I can't afford to buy hormone replacement cream anymore and I'll never be able to buy another car if I stay. As you know, I sold my car two years ago and invested the money, intending to buy another when I retired. There seemed little point in having a car sitting idle in the garage while I had the use of a company car as manager of our Harare office. What seemed a lot of money at the time would not even buy me a new TV today."

"Our weekly groceries - which we could carry out of the shop in a few bags - cost $40,000 last week. How much longer can this go on? The bottom line is that I've lost all hope that things will ever come right. Before the presidential election, it looked as though we had a chance, but now I do believe that time has run out for me. At fifty-six, I have, perhaps, ten more years of hard work left to me. I have to make a new start before it's too late."

"I wish you and Larry luck and prosperity. I wish Zimbabwe well, and pray that things will work out for all of you."

A few months later she left for Cape Town.

Even in the 1950s and 1960s the road to Beira was pitted with pot-holes and had to be reconnoitred carefully. There were swampy marshes buzzing with mosquitoes right there on the outskirts of the city. Yet, in spite of such drawbacks, Beira with its continental flavour was delightfully alluring after conservative Rhodesia. The houses were painted wild pinks, greens, blues and purples and sometimes all these colours at once. We passed the Big Bottle, that imposing advertisement for some brand of Portuguese beer, on the left. The next landmark would be the Macuti Beach lighthouse.

Finally, the sea stretched before us, the real thing after the tantalising little glimpses of grey-blue here and there between the buildings. Close to the lighthouse was The Wreck, a rusty skeleton wedged on a cluster of sharp rocks, with its prow jutting out into the sea. On we drove to the Estoril. According to legend, a fabulously wealthy entrepreneur named Carlos Britto owned this vast holiday camp. Apparently, the whole sprawling area had been reclaimed from the swamps, which explained why the mosquitoes were so bad. Mum always made us take anti-malaria tablets for three weeks before we left for Beira.

At the resort office we were allocated a chalet, one of the hundreds of very basic cement huts with corrugated iron roofs. These beehive-like structures lined the beach, row after row of them, stretching as far as the eye could see. Mum always said that the term "chalet" was a misnomer for something so ugly. She thought of "a chalet" as a picturesque little wooden building nestling among fir trees with mountains in the distance. We weren't concerned about chocolate box beauty; we just wanted somewhere to sleep at the end of a day spent on the beach. And the sea was just yards away.

The Estoril beaches were a paradise for children. The waves were gentle, and there were no rocks and no sharks. During our first tingling swim of the day we would lie in the glassy grey sea and watch the sun rise out of the water. Then, starving, we would run up to the café to buy milk and crusty Portuguese bread. There was a roller-skating rink nearby where skates could be hired when we took a break from the beach. Bumps, bruises and cuts could be soaked in the sea, when our half-hour was up.

Often, during the intense heat of the day, we would walk beyond the Estoril to the Macuti Lighthouse, climb into The Wreck and lean against its brown ribs. A sense of reverence required that we whisper as we speculated upon what had happened to the luckless ship and its crew. We sifted sandy pebbles and tiny shells through our fingers and breathed in the salty air, as we waited for the tide to come in.

In the evening, along with the other occupants of the hundreds of chalets, we would buy fish or chicken and chips from the Estoril café. Mickie Most's "Think It Over" or Cliff Richard's "D In Love" would be pounding out of the speakers. We could dance in that large outdoor area next to the skating rink. We could wear shorts or swimming costumes and walk about barefoot. When we wandered back to turn in for the night, the lighthouse beams would be sending warning tracks of brightness far out to sea. One, two, three sure, regular swings and then three in a slightly different direction would sweep across us, lighting the beach and the path to our chalet.

We loved shopping in the Chinese quarter, where we would examine dragons in many shapes and forms on vases, lanterns and bamboo curtains. Eventually, after the patience of the shopkeepers must have worn thin, we would settle upon a couple of delicately worked miniature ornaments with their dragon motifs.

Everyone who used to holiday in Beira will remember The Oceana Restaurant. It was a tradition for Rhodesians to go there at least once each holiday. The food was excellent and there was a mountain of it. Diners never ordered individually. If there were eight of you, you ordered six portions and eight plates. This was perfectly acceptable, and part of the alchemy of the place.

The behaviour of the Portuguese men was both amusing and irritating. Starved of feminine company (their women were chaperoned or kept out of sight), the men and boys would indulge in all sorts of antics on the beach to attract the attention of the women and girls. They were very obtrusive in their beach games and acrobatics. They must have loved Rhodesian school holidays when flocks of females in skimpy swimwear lay sunning themselves. We thought they were a bunch of sex-starved voyeurs, and felt haughtily superior and resentful of their invasion of *our* Estoril beach.

School holidays always passed too quickly. After a couple of weeks we had to pack up our things and head home to prepare for the new term. The journey was tedious and the potholes on the way home seemed much worse. Boarding school, a few days away, loomed on the Rhodesian side of the border.

The world will remember the terrible floods that occurred several years ago in Mozambique, and the amazing birth of a baby in a tree. But Gillian and I (and many others from our era) will remember the magic of school holidays spent in the sunshine on those sandy beaches when we didn't have a care in the world.

The St. Valentine's Day March

We loved Joan's samosas[13] and spicy Indian food. The March Book Club was at her house and we were looking forward to an exotic tea.

"This week," said Moira, "I think we've regained our national pride."

She was referring to the fact that for months Zimbabweans had been agonising about the Cricket World Cup. Debates and discussions had raged, polarising the participants. Tempers had flared, friends had been alienated, emails had circulated worldwide and letters had appeared in national and international newspapers. Should Zimbabweans of conscience support World Cup matches being played in the country, especially since everyone knew who the patron of the Zimbabwe Cricket Union[14] was?

On 10 February, just before taking the field for their match against Namibia in Harare, Zimbabwean cricketers, Andy Flower and Henry Olonga, had issued a statement condemning the intolerable situation in Zimbabwe where "many people have been unjustly imprisoned and tortured simply for expressing their opinions about what is happening in the country". They "mourned the death of democracy in our beloved Zimbabwe".

Their statement and their wearing of black armbands during the match demonstrated strongly the way most responsible Zimbabweans viewed this tournament. The ZCU (Zimbabwe Cricket Union) wanted them disciplined, but the ICC (International Cricket Council) refused to take any action.

Both popular cricketers were national icons. Henry was almost as well known in Zimbabwe for his beautiful song: "Our Zimbabwe", as he was for his prowess on the cricket field. The

---

13 A samosa is a fried or baked pastry with a savory filling such as spiced potatoes, onions, peas, lentils, ground lamb or chicken.
14 President Robert Mugabe

song had been an instant hit and Zimbabweans (if they had been allowed to vote on the issue) would have adopted it as the national anthem.

Moira loved feeding us tantalising titbits about Bulawayo's "beautiful people" (most of whom were our age). She'd been very disparaging about anyone supporting the World Cup, and this included members of her own social circle. Earlier in the week, she and Colin had attended a dinner in Harare, at which Andy and Henry had been guests.

"They're charming young men and such wonderful ambassadors," said Moira, leaning forward, to emphasise her point. "We should be very proud of both of them. They know that the government and the Zimbabwe Cricket Union are not going to take this lying down. Rumour has it that they'll have to skip the country."

All of us had been encouraged by their stand. The "great debate" had been put to rest, while the nation applauded them both on and off the field.

Joan had recently joined WOZA (Women of Zimbabwe Arise). Their mandate was to attempt (through peaceful means) to draw the attention of the world to the plight of the nation, and particularly to the suffering of women and children in Zimbabwe. We had heard that she had planned to march with other "sisters" from Harare, Bulawayo and Victoria Falls to say NO to violence and YES to love on St. Valentine's Day. While we applauded her sense of conviction, taking to the streets wasn't everyone's thing. Most of us were not political animals and our men folk certainly would never allow us to take such a risk. Joan was more of a free and independent spirit, with her husband away in Botswana.

She sat quietly while we discussed cricket issues.

"How did the march go, Joan?" asked Mary. "We heard that some women were arrested."

"They were," said Joan. "And I was one of them."

We were shocked. We'd read that there had been a police presence and that some women had been apprehended, but it had never occurred to us that Joan would be at the forefront of the action.

"My goodness!" said Moira. "While we were dining at New Orleans, with the Fosters and the Erharts, red roses decorating the table and champagne corks popping around us, you were locked up in a filthy police cell at the Central Police Station?"

"That's right," replied Joan.

We all gazed at her in disbelief. Joan was one of those tall, slim, graceful women with immaculately painted long nails: someone who was always beautifully turned out in a long dress and high-heeled shoes. The conditions in the police cells were known to be unbelievably foul, and many tales had circulated about disgusting toilets and bodies packed into tiny areas where there was no room to move. It was difficult imagining our elegant Joan in such a place.

Joan described how the singing women had handed flowers to people in the streets to symbolise their message of love and peace. She was carrying carnations and a placard on which was written "Peace; Food; Prosperity". This was the first time she'd participated in a march or demonstration, but she had reached a point in her life, she said, where she felt that she had to stand up for her beliefs. Her feelings and those of the other marchers echoed the final line of Andy and Henry's statement: "…we pray that our small action may help to restore sanity and dignity to our nation".

Like the stance taken by the two cricketers, it was, in fact, NOT "a small action". Everyone participating in the march understood that the police were likely to react violently. It would be naïve to imagine that they would be less aggressive towards a group of women.

As the women reached the junction of 8th Avenue and Main Street, riot police accosted the group and quickly surrounded them. Some of the more fortunate ladies found themselves taken hold of and gently pushed beyond the reach of the police by supportive men in the crowd. These sympathisers took their placards and flowers, threw them under parked vehicles and then formed a human shield in front of them. They were able to melt quietly away.

Joan was not one of the lucky ones. She and the other detainees were ordered into police trucks and carted off to the police station. They had decided in advance that passive resistance was in keeping with the peaceful and loving spirit of the walk. Father Nigel Johnson, who was filming the march, was viciously assaulted. His camera was forcibly removed and one policeman attempted to throttle him as they manhandled him into a truck. Onlookers were very angry at the behaviour of the police, but were intimidated by their threats and menacing gestures with huge riot batons.

The prisoners were herded into the courtyard at Bulawayo Central Police Station, where they had to stand in the hot sun without water to drink, while their names, addresses and I.D. numbers were taken down four times by different police details. After this they were put in a mesh and barbed wire enclosure in front of the holding cells. Then, in groups of five, they were taken to a small room where each woman had to remove her bra, petticoat, shoes, jewellery and spectacles. Cell phones were taken from them. By this time, lawyers had arrived. They advised the detainees not to make statements or to sign anything.

"No one would have been able to read or write anything anyway, since everyone needed spectacles," remarked Joan. "Our average age was probably 55."

Visitors brought water and fruit, and, a little later, more substantial food arrived. Everything was shared. The police supplied plates of sugar beans in a thin gruel to the male prisoners and nothing to the women. At about 6.30 pm the women were locked up. Some among them knew what to expect. Most did not.

"There is only one holding cell for women at Bulawayo Central," Joan told us. "It's about three metres by six metres in area. The squat pan is partitioned off from the cell by a metre-high wall. Twenty-two of us spent St Valentine's night in the most primitive and barbaric conditions imaginable.

We were overcome by a foul stench from the open toilet as we entered the cell. When our eyes became accustomed to the gloom, we realised that human faeces had been flung at the walls and had stuck to them. The excreta had obviously been there some time - no attempt appeared to have been made to hose the revolting mess off. Graffiti provided little light relief; there was nothing more entertaining than "Home, Sweet Home" and a few names written on the walls. Toilet paper was not provided. We were intensely relieved that a few of the women, who knew the ropes, had managed to smuggle some in.

We found ourselves wedged into this small, evil-smelling space, with three blankets to share. There wasn't enough room for everyone to lie down, so we had to position ourselves as comfortably as was possible. Some of us stood, some sat with our legs drawn up to our chins. Periodically, we would change places with one another. The blankets swarmed with fleas, bed bugs and lice. We were painfully aware of creatures crawling over us and of the need to scratch. Perhaps having to hand over our bras wasn't such a bad idea, after all."

I shuddered inwardly as I listened to Joan's narrative. Being locked up in a confined space in the dark was the worst thing I could imagine. Many years before, I had bought Patty Hearst's story for Book Club. Patty Hearst, a nineteen–year-old Californian heiress had been kidnapped by a terrorist group, the SLA (the Symbionese Liberation Army). Her captors had kept her blindfolded and shut up in a closet for two months. Convinced that the only way to survive lay in "renouncing her past", Patty had participated in "re-education classes". These qualified her to become an urban guerrilla. I was sure that I would have participated in a bank robbery too, if I'd suffered this type of sensory deprivation. That's if I hadn't gone stark raving mad long before that.

I focused again on what Joan was saying. She was still describing the cell the women had occupied.

"There were two panes of glass high up near the ceiling, and these allowed dim light from the sanitary lane outside to seep through. The shutter over the peephole in the door was broken, so one person at a time could look through this and report on what was happening outside to anyone who was interested."

During the night Joan observed various members of the police force carrying about the rare commodities of maize meal, oil, bread and cotton wool. They obviously weren't suffering too seriously from the shortages afflicting everyone else.

"One of the WOZA leaders encouraged us to sing hymns and songs during the earlier stages of the evening. This helped to keep everyone's spirits up, and to pass the time. The boredom was what disturbed me more than anything else. It was awful having no idea what the time was and having absolutely nothing to do. I kept listening for the chimes of the city hall clock, but this proved futile. The clock only chimes during the day, it seems. Or perhaps it stopped chiming long ago and needs to be fixed. Perhaps we haven't even noticed that it's been silent for ages.

As the night wore on, two drunken women were thrown into the cell. At least, they appeared to be drunk, but I think they might have been plants, there to report any careless remarks. They behaved very badly, shouting and yelling, and, worst of all, they hogged the peephole. On two or three occasions the policemen on duty herded us out of the cell to be counted. We tried to confuse the police regarding numbers, so that we could stay outside as long as possible. It reminded me of the TV series 'Tenko' - that Japanese internment camp for women.

Finally, at about 5.30 am on Saturday morning, we were allowed out of the cell. Relatives and friends were there to greet us with breakfast and welcome flasks of tea. Father Nigel was delighted to find that black coffee and cigarettes had been brought for him. It was wonderful to know that we had not been abandoned and that people were concerned and aware of our situation. Shortly after 8 am the lawyers returned, more forms were filled in, and, finally, we were allowed to leave.

We tend to take many simple things for granted. That night I learned how important it is to be able to open a door for myself, how wonderful to flush a toilet and brush my teeth. The experience of having to squat barefoot on a wet floor over a pan to urinate was not something I want to repeat in a hurry.

When I got home, I showered over and over again, but couldn't seem to dislodge the dreadful stench from my hair and body. It seemed to have permeated every pore. I made a small bonfire and burned every bit of clothing I'd worn on the march."

"Wow!" said Marilyn. "Would you ever do such a thing again? I certainly couldn't have coped with that revolting filth."

Joan didn't hesitate. "I will do everything in my power to promote love and peace in Zimbabwe. I truly believe that it's up to the women of this country to set an example. It's imperative that Zimbabweans refuse to tolerate violence and oppression, particularly when it's directed at women."

"These buggers don't give a damn about the rights of women and children," said Colleen. "I can't see the point of marching and being locked up. I mean, what does it achieve? It's probably a game to them – they love flexing their muscles."

Mary disagreed. "We have to stand our ground and insist on our right to demonstrate peacefully. There was a courageous group of people who demonstrated at the first cricket match in Bulawayo. They were locked up, too."

"It's vital that the rest of the world knows what is going on in Zim," I said. "The international press is here in force to report on the cricket. It's a wonderful opportunity, and we should make the most of it."

Colleen was not convinced, however. She felt that demonstrations and disobedience fed the government's desire for reprisals and revenge.

Once again, we'd spent more time discussing current events than we had reviewing books. At work you had to watch what you said. You never knew who might be listening: the cleaner you thought you could trust; the person hovering outside your office door waiting to request leave to attend his uncle's funeral; the caterers bringing lunch for the workers; the postman delivering the mail.

It was safe to talk politics at Book Club.

ROUND AND AROUND WE GO

21 September 2003.

Richard and Trevor were looking glum when I walked into their office yesterday. Their messenger had gone to the bank to collect the wages and had been told to come back on Monday or maybe Tuesday, as there was no cash available. Their workers were refusing to leave until they'd been paid. Could we lend them the money?

Last week we bought cash from Costa's supermarket. We needed $5,000,000 for our wages, and had to give him a cheque for that amount plus an extra 15%. There are queues outside every bank and building society. People are desperately trying to draw their own money.

A few weeks ago the government announced that, as of 26 September, all the current red $500 notes would be withdrawn and replaced with new $500 notes. They've been running full-page ads in all the papers to "introduce" the new $500 note and the new $1,000 note that's supposed to come into effect on 1 October. Will the new notes be ready for circulation? Where did they get the money to print them? Where's the logic in the decision to substitute one type of $500 note for another?

They've been trying to force us to part with our cash, so that money circulates once again. No one has been depositing cash, of course, since it's in such short supply. We're holding onto what little we have. You have to have cash to buy fuel.

Dennis' pumps next door have been dry for months. So he's diversified – he sells bread instead. On the street outside our front door, fuel is available from five or six black market vendors. The smell of the petrol being siphoned into cooking oil bottles, vodka bottles and paraffin bottles from drums on the back of trucks is vile. But we can't keep our office windows shut - it's far too hot.

There's going to be an accident soon. I've seen some of those vendors smoking.

25 September

Will we wake up on 27 September to find that red $500 notes are worth less than $10 notes? There doesn't seem to be a plan for phasing out the old notes and bringing in the new ones.

I remember a morning, many years ago, when we woke up to find that all the street names in central Bulawayo had changed. Selborne Avenue had miraculously become Leopold Takawira Avenue, Rhodes Street was now George Silundika, Wilson Street was Josiah Tongogara and Borrow Street had become Samuel Parirenyatwa. Municipal employees had obviously been working like beavers all night. They couldn't fit "Samuel Parirenyatwa" onto the standard metal street sign, so they had used two and joined them together. Grey Street, that runs through town and continues out to the airport, had become Robert Mugabe Way.

Overnight, we've acquired a Robert Mugabe Street, Road or Way in most of our cities and towns.

A circular email is doing the rounds reminding us that a $10 note is worth less than a square of toilet paper, and that we should use this instead to save money. It's quite a good idea, since toilet paper is so scarce.

4 October

We've been given a reprieve. We can continue to use our old red $500 notes, which they'll phase out sometime...

This is par for the course. They'll make some grand pronouncement that's obviously not going to work. When a crisis of monumental proportions threatens, they do an about turn, and life goes on...

Part V

DRIVING OUT THE RUBBISH

2005

DEFEATED ONCE MORE

18 April 2005
Zimbabwe is twenty-five today.

We're still trying to recover from the parliamentary elections two weeks ago, after ZANU PF "secured" 78 seats, leaving the MDC with only 41. Jonathan Moyo (formerly spin doctor extraordinaire for the government) in his new role as an independent won the Tsholotsho North seat.

Today the Party faithful will gather to celebrate another glorious year. They'll sing, dance, revile the whites and gloat about the MDC's failure to retain its seats. (There's only 20,000 of us left now. In 1978, two years before independence, there were 270,000.) The President will pour scorn on Tony Blair and honour our latest hero, a man who conveniently committed suicide a few days ago. And soon they'll distribute the last few farms to those cronies who served them well in orchestrating the theft of the election.

It's business as usual.

The MDC had to think long and hard about whether or not to boycott this election. They knew that every dirty trick in the ZANU PF arsenal would be used against them. If they chose not to stand, and allowed a ZANU PF walk-over, the opposition would no longer have a voice in parliament. On the other hand, if they fielded their candidates and lost through vote rigging, it would appear that the party no longer enjoyed the support of the electorate.

Classic Catch 22.

During the run-up, MDC crowds from Chimanimani to Harare, from Bulawayo to Binga and from Marondera to Chiredzi came out in their thousands and tens of thousands to support their candidates.

Their rallies are always entertaining. Young people wearing MDC T-shirts put on energetic displays of dancing and acrobatics. The singing is brilliant. Political rhetoric is good-humoured and there is much laughter and gesturing with the open palm party salute.

The stars of the show in Bulawayo, if Morgan can't attend, are usually David Coltart and Welshman Ncube. They're sometimes joined by Gibson Sibanda, the Vice President, a roly-poly, jovial personality. It makes no difference that Dave is white. The crowds love him.

When the results were announced, the western world condemned the obvious theft of another election. Within days, though, other issues intruded as they always did: the war in Iraq escalated; the problems of the EU intensified; the election in Britain was imminent; and Charles was marrying Camilla. The death and funeral of Pope John Paul II and the intriguing election of his successor effectively eliminated any residual interest in our stolen election.

It's beginning to look as though ZANU PF is here to stay.

The strangest book we'd read in recent months was "Life of Pi" by Yann Martel, a Canadian author.

"Bizarre," said Jeanette.

"Compelling," said Shirley.

"Ridiculous, absolutely absurd," said Margaret.

"Fascinating," said Colleen. "I loved every word of it."

"Take Hinduism, Islam and Catholicism. Add a Bengal tiger, an Indian boy of 16 and a lifeboat. Lose them at sea. Stir in several large spoonfuls of zoology and philosophy. Allow concoction to simmer for 227 days and you'll have a Booker prize-winning story."

That was Mary's take on the novel.

Geraldine said that she had no intention of reading a book about a boy who survives being cast adrift with a zebra, a hyena, an orang-utan and a tiger called Richard Parker weighing 450 pounds. She'd rather read "Charlie and the Chocolate Factory" to her sons.

I'd found the story audacious but enthralling. I loved the ending, where Pi invites the officials from the shipping company to choose which of his two narratives they prefer. The only part I didn't enjoy was the island of carnivorous algae and meerkats.

It isn't easy to discuss the recent elections without getting depressed or entangled in arguments. Many of our Book Club members used to be enthusiastic (though not necessarily active) MDC supporters. Now they're either disillusioned or resentful.

Joan did her best to defend the MDC yesterday.

"Don't be too critical," she said. "ZANU PF has billions of dollars at its disposal. The CIO[15] is using much of it to infiltrate opposition structures. We all know that the MDC has no access to the radio, television or to a daily newspaper. 'The Daily News' no longer exists. They've succeeded in jamming SW Radio, Africa. So how do we reach the people? We all know that the government uses food as its most effective weapon. If our rural folk don't toe the line it's very simple. They don't eat."

"For God's sake," Colleen said, "if the black people simply put up with things as they are, the western powers will think this is the government they want. They have to send a message to the world that they're not happy. Zimbabweans have ostensibly re-elected ZANU PF. They've got no backbone, these blacks."

Book Club was at Geraldine's house. Although the days were getting cooler, it was warm on her veranda. Shirley was leaning against the railing in the sunshine smoking a cigarette. Colleen was trying to give up smoking. She watched Shirley for a while, and then decided to join her. To hell with it, a cigarette would help her to relax. She'd stop tomorrow.

"It's easy for those of us who live in town to be critical," Margaret responded. "We sit safely behind our electric fences and electric gates. Our houses have bars on every window and many of us have intruder alarms and panic buttons. Imagine what it must be like living in a hut in a remote rural village where there's no safety or security. These poor people are so vulnerable."

---

15 The CIO: The feared Central Intelligence Organisation

"I know, I know," said Colleen blowing out a cloud of smoke. She was feeling better already, and her hands had stopped shaking. "But it's so frustrating. Until they take to the streets in huge numbers, things won't change."

"The people know that if they go into the streets, they'll be arrested," said Joan. "Look what happened to me. But that was small stuff. Just a warning to a group of irritating, presumptuous women. The police would be out in force, as would the army with all the sophisticated riot gear they've bought. The streets would run with blood."

"Where's the merit in dying for a cause pointlessly?" asked Shirley, sitting down again. She was looking cool in fashionable pink shorts that she'd bought on her last trip to South Africa. "America, the UN and Britain would issue a statement condemning the 'contemptible act' and then they'd focus their attention on the Middle East again."

It was obvious to all of us – even to Joan - that the opposition leadership had not taken advantage of its many opportunities to protest effectively. There had been occasions when they could have rallied the people, who would have followed them gladly and bravely. (After the first election was stolen, for example, the people had been eager to translate their anger and disappointment into action.)

"There's no point in us demonstrating outside State House," said Geraldine. "A few conspicuous white faces would make excellent targets. Getting involved in this type of protest would achieve nothing. I've no desire to throw myself needlessly in front of ZANU's artillery. I wouldn't be much good to my family riddled with bullets."

We shelved politics after Geraldine's comment. It was time for tea, anyway. Geraldine disliked baking. Every year, Glenda gave her an unusual, very practical birthday present. They agreed that when it was Geraldine's turn to host Book Club, Glenda would do the baking for her. Glenda's micro-waved chocolate cake was delicious, as was her bee-sting - a cake with a sticky honey, cream and almond topping. I always meant to ask Geraldine what she gave Glenda for *her* birthday.

Geraldine's two young sons wandered in and out of the dining room. They loved Book Club teas. I loved Geraldine's pictures. My favourite - a gnarled log that had fallen across a bush track - hung in her lounge. Whenever Book Club was at her house, I was drawn to this picture.

Margaret came to join me in the lounge and we sat down to chat. The dining room was very noisy. She and Matthew were planning to spend three weeks in their flat at Umhlanga in June. They were looking forward to walks on the beach and to shopping for Christmas presents for their grandchildren.

ZIMBABWE'S TSUNAMI

24 May

The ruling party is determined to make Zimbabwe a better and safer place for everyone, particularly for those of us who live in the cities and towns. So the police are carrying out a massive "exercise" to eliminate or "clean up" and "drive out" the "filth" and the "rubbish". The government is concerned about crime in the cities.

"Operation Murambatsvina" is actually a declaration of war on black urban dwellers, who have consistently supported the MDC in every election since 2000. Specifically targeted are small traders like "tuckshop" owners, vegetable sellers, flower sellers, curio sellers, tinkers and people running flea market stalls. Waves of armed police have been sent in to burn or confiscate their produce and to wreck their stalls, so that they can no longer trade. This is because they are "unlicensed".

In some areas people have been forced to tear down their own homes; in others the police have used bulldozers, sledgehammers and flamethrowers to demolish them. These buildings are not just shacks - many are brick dwellings, for which "no planning permission has been sought or granted".

The wreckers have chopped up their furniture and torched or stolen their possessions. Distraught families have been left picking through rubble, in an attempt to recover something ... anything...

Slums must be cleared away. The "filth" must be removed.

2 June

In Hatcliffe Extension, Harare, Muslims have been forced by the police at gunpoint to destroy their own mosque. A Catholic orphanage and clinic housing 180 AIDS orphans was bulldozed to rubble. AIDS sufferers on antiretroviral (ARV) drug programmes are now homeless. Without their drugs, they will die.

We're not talking about a squatter camp. During the last sitting of Parliament, a resolution was unanimously passed upgrading Hatcliffe Extension to the status of a legal settlement. And, because it *was* a legal housing area, the World Bank financed the development of a water supply and sewerage works for the suburb.

They've destroyed more than 6,000 homes.

13 June
Early yesterday morning, police riot squads moved into Killarney a few kilometres down the road from us. There were about 800 people living in an informal settlement which has been there for over twenty years. They were given minutes to leave their houses before they were torched.

It was freezing cold.

Bulawayo churches have, as usual, done everything they can to help. They're providing shelter and feeding these poor people until the government undertakes to re-locate them. Stella says that the police have accused the churches of trying to make the government "look bad".

This isn't only happening in the cities. We've heard that the six kilometre line of curio stalls on the Victoria Falls Road has been set ablaze and destroyed in their "clean-up" exercise. What must it have been like for those curio sellers to watch their beautiful creations going up in flames?

Augustine Chihuri, our police commissioner, has explained that his objective is to "clean the country of the crawling mass of maggots bent on destroying the economy". Mugabe says it's "a vigorous clean-up campaign to restore order in urban areas". Ironically, (in our crime-ridden society), these are the very people who have been attempting to make an honest living and who provide a service to their communities.

Where will they go?

The government says they should return to their rural homes.

Many are not Zimbabweans and have no family in the rural areas. They're from Malawi, South Africa, Zambia, Mozambique and Botswana. They've probably lived in the towns and cities all their lives.

4 July

"How will they get 'home' to the rural areas?" asked Mary. "They have no money. There's no fuel, so there are no buses available to transport them. They've been left to roam the streets with nowhere to go and with nothing to eat."

"Without shelter, many of them, especially the babies will die," said Joan sadly. "Can you imagine what it's like out in the open at night now in the middle of winter? Obviously part of the master plan. Eliminate the rubbish. Get rid of the Jews. It's terrifying."

"We've been receiving all sorts of emails promising 'action'," said Jeanette. "These hint that the 'action' will become clearer as 'events unfold'. I know that to be specific would be considered subversive, and I appreciate that calls to 'action' have to be cautious. We've been told to 'remain at home for the next two days'. They go on to say 'the stay-away has the support of all major civic bodies in the country. We will be protesting in a way that will not expose people to the violence and intimidation of the police and army'."

I felt sure that the result of this new 'call to action' would be yet another unofficial public holiday. The workers might rejoice, but the business sector had become increasingly cynical about the likely success of such events. What was the point of closing businesses for two days or longer, and of letting employees have time off to register their protests, if the whole process fizzled out like a damp squib?

Larry, Sean and I believed that the commercial and industrial sector was culpable, as well, because a large number of businesses were not prepared to pay those workers who wished to observe the stay-away. "Managers, who took this approach, believed that their employees should be prepared to sacrifice their wages during the stay-away for the good of their country and its people." Others insisted that workers wishing to stay away took leave. Their factory and office doors would remain open, but their workers were at liberty to follow their consciences. This sitting on the fence on the part of business neither offered a positive answer, nor constituted any kind of moral stance.

"I heard that a group of protesters who approached a police road block were told that if the people came in their tens, they would be turned back. If they came in their hundreds, the police would let them through. If they came in their thousands and tens of thousands, the police would join them!" Joan said. "After all, the ordinary rank and file in the police must have many relatives whose homes and livelihoods have been destroyed."

"The MDC's vacillating and posturing reminds me of 'Horatius'," Margaret remarked:

> *"Was none who would be foremost*
> *To lead such dire attack:*
> *But those behind cried 'Forward!'*
> *And those before cried 'Back!'*
> *And backward now and forward*
> *Wavers the deep array;*
> *And on the tossing sea of steel,*
> *To and fro the standards reel;*
> *And the victorious trumpet-peal*
> *Dies fitfully away."*

"I wish we had a Nelson Mandela in this country," said Mary forlornly.

"Not that gutless Mbeki with his 'quiet diplomacy'," Colleen said viciously. "South Africa could have stopped all this years ago."

I'd driven past the City Hall the previous day.

Ever since I could remember, the pavement on Fife Street between Selborne (now Leopold Takawira) and 8ᵗʰ Avenue had been awash with colour and bustling with flower-sellers, artists, sculptors, bead workers and basket weavers. Tourists would stroll through the City Hall gardens to browse among rows of fat wooden hippos, soapstone statues of mother and child and intricately patterned baskets. After running their hands over their chosen hippo's stout flanks, and having held the bead necklaces up to the light, they would commence the necessary bargaining rituals. And we Bulawayo people would sometimes find the time to stop and buy a bunch of roses on the way home from work. I must confess to having felt irritated on occasion at the unruly mass of people spilling onto the road. I felt ashamed of this unworthy sentiment now.

Yesterday there was an empty street and a bare grey pavement. Not a single person, not a single flower, not one basket or necklace. The vendors had been chased away - vermin, who needed to be eradicated. Pieces of paper and tattered plastic bags swirled about in the wind.

Many years ago I saw the film "On the Beach". A nuclear war had obliterated humanity in the Northern Hemisphere. Radiation sickness resulting from this holocaust had spread relentlessly southwards, killing everyone. Melbourne, Australia was one of the last large concentrations of doomed people. Gradually communication with the rest of the world was lost. One of the final radio broadcasts the people of Melbourne heard was from Salisbury, Rhodesia, as the population of our country succumbed to the inevitable.

The closing scene of the film has haunted me ever since. The streets of Melbourne were completely deserted. Brisk winds blew old newspapers about...

THE PASSPORT OFFICE

"You know what my kids are like," said Mary. "There's always a drama. Usually medical, unfortunately. We've had to rush down to South Africa several times now. Having Zimbabwean passports is a nightmare; they cause problems wherever you go in the world. Immigration officials always send us to the back of the queue, whether we're in Johannesburg, London or Croatia.

The boys' passports have to be renewed in September, so I decided to do the sensible and responsible thing and get organised in good time. Glenda told me that she had found the procedures fairly straight forward if you had all the necessary documentation ready, so I took careful note of what was required. I had to have the children's birth certificates, passport photos, my ID, Mark's ID and a letter of permission from Mark. Original documents have to be produced along with certified copies. All this to enable me to collect an application form for each child.

I'd heard daunting reports that standing in a queue to achieve this could be a ten-day affair. I'd been given the name of a lady, who might be willing to assist me, if I could get into the passport office building. When I arrived there, I was confronted by the anticipated queue. I strode purposefully to the front, trying to ignore the glares and mutterings of those who had probably spent several nights waiting in line. I told the guard that I had an appointment with Mrs Ngwenya and slipped into the reception area, while he was wondering whether or not to let me in. 'Act confident,' I thought.

The receptionist directed me to Room 3. I found my way there and greeted the occupants brightly. 'I've come to see Mrs Ngwenya,' I said."

'She's not here.'

'Oh,' I said dumbfounded. 'Where is she?'

'On leave.'

'Are you sure?'

'Yes.'

'When will she be back?'

'Uuh. Two weeks.'

'Their responses were grumpy and unfriendly. It was difficult to know how to react. 'Well, I'm sure you can help me,' I said, ingratiatingly. 'I've come to collect application forms so that I can renew my sons' passports.'

'Go to Central Hospital,' one of the women said, without raising her eyes from the hunk of bread she was eating."

'But this is the passport office, isn't it?' I questioned, perplexed.

'So?'

'Well surely, this is the place where I can get forms?'

'No,' said the lady, her mouth crammed full of bread. She took a large gulp from a mug of tea to wash the food down. 'We've decentralised. Go to Tredgold Building or to Central Hospital.'

The seething, impenetrable mass of humanity outside Tredgold Building was discouraging, to say the least. So I resolved to pluck up my courage and try the Hospital. As you all know, the Central Hospital covers a very large area and there are a number of different sections ranging from the Blood Transfusion Centre to Infectious Diseases. Where to start? There were no signs anywhere. A very pleasant gardener directed me to the Outpatients' Clinic, an old colonial-style single storey building, some distance away from the main hospital.

On the veranda, a clinic was in session. Patients were perched on the low wall in the sunshine; some of the men with their shirts off and their trousers turned up. A doctor was examining them right there, out in the open, listening to a chest, winding the bandage off a foot, peering into infected eyes. An old broken bookcase separated these people from the rest of the area. On the other side of this division, a guard was running a tuck-shop selling superkools, sweets and biscuits to the weary mob. I had to squeeze past him to follow his vague directions to a room further down the dingy corridor. I attempted to join the line of people at the far end, only to discover that I was actually jumping the queue. A female guard directed me to a room to the side...

...Where I found myself in the breast-feeding clinic! There were a few old, slatted benches arranged back to back as if we were at a bus stop or poised for a game of musical chairs. Mothers in night-gowns nursing tiny new-born infants faced one way, while facing the other way were those, like me, who required application forms for passports and for birth and death certificates. The mothers evidently needed advice from medical staff who were nowhere to be seen. I was struck (as I always am) by the quiet patience (or passivity) of the waiting women. No one was demanding attention. Black people seem so much more accepting than their white counterparts.

The fact that swollen milk-filled breasts were very much in evidence was simply not an issue. The mothers got on with their very different concerns in a world far removed from ours.

I soon began to enjoy myself. A large lady announced loudly and belligerently that no one was going to jump the queue; she would personally eject anyone who attempted to do so. I wouldn't have stood a chance if she had decided to remove me earlier.

We all chatted and swapped experiences. A young white guy told us that he was a hunter, operating on contract in Tanzania. Their camp had burnt down while he and his clients were out on a hunt. Everything, including their passports, had been destroyed. Much to his astonishment, he had succeeded in getting an emergency travel document within twenty-four hours in Dar es Salaam. The attitude of the Zimbabwean authorities, however, was a little less helpful. They told him that he'd have to wait six months before handing in his application form for a replacement passport. He had to 'pay the penalty' for 'destroying' his passport.

The large lady leapt up intermittently and demanded to know what was happening in the corridor. It became something of a joke, and each time we moved up a place on the benches, there were celebratory cheers. Even the guard entered into our spirit of fun, as we waved enthusiastically at her, asking for a progress report.

The three ladies in the inner sanctum, when I finally got there, were charming. They processed my documents efficiently and politely, and, at last, I had the two forms in my hand. Now the real nightmare will begin. Next I will have to have the boys' fingerprints taken and hire someone to sleep in a queue for several nights so that more forms can be processed.

Throughout this experience, I was struck by the thought that so often in our country, tragedy and chaos and humour and patience are juxtaposed. There was a warmth and camaraderie that transcended race and political affiliation, since no one was immune from ridiculous bureaucracy and cavalier treatment. The word 'bizarre' must be one of the most frequently used adjectives in Zimbabwe today. I was also aware, though, that we really *are* living in a fourth world country in deepest, darkest Africa, and that Zimbabwe has joined the ranks of such places as Liberia and Rwanda.

We never thought we'd get to this point, but I'm afraid that we have."

HUMANITARIAN CRISIS

23 July

Mrs. Anna Kajumulo Tibaijuka, the UN special envoy, sent to Zimbabwe by Kofi Annan himself to study the impact of the "campaign" to "restore order" has published her findings[16]. We're delighted to hear that she wasn't taken in by the government's contemptible efforts to portray their demolition campaign as a "development initiative". She condemned the wanton destruction of homes which, she said, had left 700,000 people homeless or jobless and affected at least 2.4 million people, precipitating a humanitarian crisis. *"Cleaning of cities cannot be an event, it has to be a process,"* she said.

Her conclusion was that *"while purporting to target illegal dwellings and structures and to clamp down on alleged illicit activities, (the operation) was carried out in an indiscriminate and unjustified manner, with indifference to human suffering..."*

We had expected to hear formal condemnation earlier in the month from the G8 Summit at Gleneagles in Scotland. "The Independent" newspaper reported that world leaders had fiercely denounced Mugabe. President Putin was reported to have said that Western countries should stop subsidising the corruption and incompetence of inept dictators. Even President Mbeki was reported to be shuffling toward some sort of stance on our humanitarian crisis.

It seemed that world leaders were about to take a firmer approach.

Then fate intervened, once more.

On the second day of the summit, during the morning rush hour, three bombs exploded within fifty seconds of each other

16 Report of the Fact-Finding Mission to Zimbabwe to assess the Scope and Impact of Operation Murambatsvina by the UN Special Envoy on Human Settlements Issues in Zimbabwe. Mrs. Anna Kajumulo Tibaijuka. 17 June 2005.

on three London Underground trains. A fourth exploded an hour later at 09:47 on a double-decker bus. Fifty-six people were killed, including the bombers, and 700 were injured.

30 July

The week ended on a ludicrous note.

Dennis, next door, had to borrow 5 litres of fuel from us to get home. He's been waiting for a delivery of fuel promised ages ago.

6 August

Yesterday, much to everyone's surprise and delight, a large tanker delivered fuel to Dennis' service station.

We kept craning out of the window to watch the drama unfolding in the street outside the factory. Was it petrol or was it diesel? We weren't kept in suspense long. Those huge grey pied pipers always attract the appropriate vehicles. Within moments of its arrival, the guzzlers - emergency taxis, buses, trucks and pantechnicons were swarming all over the road.

It was diesel.

Some of our cars were parked directly outside and there was a mad scramble to get them out of the way of the queue that was beginning to form, and into the centre parking area. (This is when we Bulawayo people really appreciate the wide streets of our city.) If we hadn't moved them immediately, we'd have been hemmed in for hours on a Friday afternoon.

The reek of diesel was overpowering, as fumes from buses idling outside poured through the doors and windows. But we weren't complaining.

At the beginning of the week, Charles took four drums of fuel up to Harare.

"I had to go through six road blocks," he told us. "When the police stopped me, I smiled and asked them how they were and how the job was. I got them talking about themselves. When they saw a happy, smiling person, they didn't ask me any questions about what I was carrying in the back of the truck. I didn't even have to produce the police clearance from Bulawayo."

It was a relief to have him back safely with our fuel worth millions of dollars successfully delivered. Sean spends a large part of his working day trying to source black market fuel, so that we don't come to a grinding halt. It's illegal to transport fuel in containers... you are "hoarding". So Sean's fuel could have been confiscated by police at one of many roadblocks and Charles might have found himself spending a few nights in jail. We had managed to get an official clearance from Larry's police contact, but we had no idea whether police personnel at the other end of the country would honour it.

As soon as the tanker left, Sean and Charles drove our two diesel bakkies[17] to the "Accounts" queue round the corner. After a while, they realised that nothing was happening – the queue wasn't moving. Sean went to investigate, and found that the only diesel pump wasn't working. It had been out of action so long, that it had seized up. Dennis wasn't around. He'd probably gone off to have a couple of beers to celebrate his fuel delivery. There was a crazy scramble to locate a mechanic – not an easy task on a Friday afternoon. Eventually, the problem was solved, and by 4.30 pm the line of vehicles began to move.

15 August

We hear that certain "selected" service stations will have fuel delivered to them by NOCZIM (the National Oil Company of Zimbabwe). They'll be required to pay for this in US$, and no questions will be asked as to the origin of the currency.

We're confused.

We've been threatened with all kinds of penalties if we're found in possession of foreign currency.

One reason for eliminating "the rubbish" was to get rid those dealing illegally in foreign currency.

---

17 Bakkie – A small truck with an open body and low sides (from Afrikaans: *bak* – container).

STELLA

At the last two or three Book Club meetings, Joan had commented savagely on men who were unable to look after themselves. "They are so bloody useless on their own," she would say. "Jeff has never learned to cook. All he does is open tins. No wonder he's sick of corned beef and ham. He's also drinking far too much. I don't know why he doesn't hire a domestic. He loves his steak and boerewors[18]: anyone can cook those."

"Not as well as you can," we reminded her. A piece of fillet or rump would be tenderised in a spicy marinade for days before being grilled to exquisite perfection in Joan's kitchen. Her curries were legendary. Of course he wanted her with him.

Jeff was tired of living alone in a one-horse town in Botswana, where he was working twelve hours a day to earn foreign currency for their retirement. He missed his wife and thought it was about time she came to cook and keep house for him. Commuting back and forth for weekends (which entailed travelling hundreds of kilometres on Botswana's busy roads) was burdensome and he had finally put his foot down. Although he tried not to be too dictatorial and alarmist, he was also concerned about her involvement with WOZA. Since her arrest on St. Valentine's Day 2003, she had been detained for short periods on two other occasions. It was just a matter of time, in his opinion, before they decided to charge her and other activists under some draconian law and sentence them to prison for a couple of months. Besides, he felt she was rather enjoying doing her own thing without him.

Joan was not impressed at being coerced into moving to the dust and heat of Mahalapye, somewhere in Botswana's outback. Despite her dissatisfaction, they'd agreed to rent their house to friends until they were ready to return either to retire or to

---

18 Boerewors: a large, spicy homemade sausage. Afrikaans: *boere* – farmers; *wors* – sausage.

sell up, depending on how the political and economic situation panned out.

"What will I do without my garden?" she wailed. "That's where I spend all my free time. How can he expect me to put up with life in a dust bowl?"

Their house was built on a rocky site in Hillside, with a magnificent view of Bulawayo. It was a unique home with several verandas and patios, from which one could gaze upon the panorama below. Beautifully groomed terraced gardens set among the rocks descended steeply from each outdoor living area. There were beds of roses, tropical ferns collected from all over the country, scores of different shrubs, lilies, fuchsias, irises and variegated petunias. Violets and pansies flourished in sections of the holding walls. Joan's touch could be seen everywhere, from the explosive colour combinations of the flowers to the rich, dark soil that had been brought in to replace the less fertile soil among the rocks.

Small wonder she was distraught at having to leave their lovely home. It was some compensation, though, that the property was being entrusted to the care of friends who, she was confident, would maintain her gardens.

"Never mind Botswana's famous lady detective, Precious Ramotswe, Africa's Miss Marple, cheerful private investigator of 'traditional build'," Jeff was reported to have said. "I've seldom read anything more ridiculous. Tswana women are totally subservient to their men folk. They work their butts off, while the men sit around smoking and drinking beer. I want you back here, my girl, away from the feminist movements. You have a husband to consider. I'm tired of driving backwards and forwards to be with you. It's your turn to contribute to our US$ nest egg."

What could Joan say? She'd been living a life of relative ease for three years, while Jeff had been slaving away in distant Mahalapye, making "real" bucks.

I had the perfect person in mind to replace Joan. Besides being an enthusiastic reader, her commitment to trying to do something positive for Zimbabwe's women had been an example to us. We all had a tendency to bury our heads in the sand if we could. My friend, Stella could be guaranteed to jolt us from our stupor.

I put her name forward.

Some ladies had heard of her. She was known to be outspoken, tireless in her pursuit of democracy and justice and extremely courageous. Although a few were wary of having an overt political presence in our midst, they agreed that we should invite her to join us.

Stella was rather nervous when she arrived for her first Book Club meeting.

"Please don't expect me to read more than one book a month," she warned the group. "I have to attend so many meetings that I seldom have time to do anything else. I worry that I am a lousy wife and mother. But because I feel that people deserve better lives, I'm prepared to give up as much time as I can to make this happen."

Stella was an attractive woman with long brown hair and blue eyes that sparkled with enthusiasm as she talked. When she was unhappy or depressed, her mouth would turn down at the corners just like the mouths on the sad little faces children draw. She wept easily, but her tears were for the poor, the tortured and the deprived – not for herself. I was very proud to be her friend.

Everyone was curious to know more about her. What had prompted her to become so involved in politics? Did her activities cause friction within her family? Were the other members of her family as committed as she was? Was she ever afraid?

Stella told us that she made a conscious resolution on her fortieth birthday that her life was going to be different. This day, she decided, would mark a new beginning in her life, and not simply a continuation. She had been suddenly overwhelmed, she said, by the reality of the elemental struggle between Good and Evil in Zimbabwe. She was determined that she would do more with her life.

Stella and David Coltart's wife, Jenny, had been friends since school. She told us how, in January 2000, David had invited interested persons to a meeting about President Mugabe's proposed new constitution. Saying "yes" to what was on the table, he said, would give President Mugabe the right to hold office for another ten years. Mugabe had declared that Britain, as the colonial power, was responsible for the payment of compensation for land seized - land could be expropriated without consultation. Such sections of the Draft Constitution had had the effect of jolting us whites out of our normal state of sluggishness, as we all remembered.

Stella's political career began with the handing out of fliers outside the MDC's offices in an entirely black part of Bulawayo urging the public to vote "no".

One evening, while in a petrol queue, she found herself listening to a prosperous-looking black gentleman whose luxurious Mercedes Benz was being filled at the pump.

"You must all vote 'yes'," he was saying to the garage attendants. "ZANU PF will look after you little guys."

"Excuse me, that is not true," Stella said indignantly. "We are all equal. There are no *little guys*. We must vote 'no'. The people are being fed lies."

The wealthy gentleman was taken aback by this challenge from a white person. The garage attendants were speechless. White persons were seldom open about their political affiliations. They certainly would never air their opinions in the presence of black strangers, who might report controversial comments to the CIO. After all, blacks had been in charge for the past twenty years. Stella was amazed at her own daring and sense of empowerment.

After the Referendum, David Coltart had announced that he would stand as the MDC's candidate for the Bulawayo South constituency. He appealed for people to assist him in his election campaign.

"I withdrew from my private nursing practice, and Terry and I took on the campaign's publicity portfolio. The MDC was about to take over our lives," said Stella.

Posters had to be put up late at night and fliers distributed clandestinely in all kinds of ingenious ways, as MDC members risked harassment or arrest by the police and confiscation of printed material.

The life Stella had been leading was radically different from the lives of most urban white women. She and Terry had had skirmishes with the police and had had to hide at a "safe house" (ours) for several days when it seemed that they were going to be picked up. Both had been in jail.

Colleen, as usual, was very sceptical about the MDC. "Give that lot half a chance and they'll be jumping on the gravy train just like every other black politician," she told Stella rather belligerently. "Power corrupts. They're just telling us what they think we want to hear."

"As I've said before, I don't believe that we whites have a place in politics here or anywhere else in Africa," said Geraldine. "We should concentrate on small things that are achievable, and leave them to sort out the big picture."

Stella opened her mouth to object, but Diana decided to defuse the situation before we moved beyond lady-like disagreement.

"My daughter emailed me very good joke last week," she said. "It goes like this...

An Englishman, a Frenchman and a World Bank economist are viewing a painting of Adam and Eve frolicking in the Garden of Eden.

'Look at their reserve, their calm,' muses the Englishman. 'They must be English.'

'Nonsense,' says the Frenchman. 'They are naked and beautiful. They must be French.'

'You are both wrong,' says the World Bank economist. 'They have no clothes and no shelter. They have only an apple to eat and they're being told they're in Paradise. Clearly they are Zimbabweans.'

So Diana, usually one of our quieter members, had the last word on this occasion.

CHERYL AND THE CID

Cheryl was another new member.

I had first met her when she came into our studio and announced that she needed letterheads for Garden Park and she'd like us to print them free of charge. She was raising money for an entertainment complex, where the elderly residents could watch TV and play bridge. The next time I saw her, she was working with Barry on a design for labels that were to go on jars of honey. I learned that she kept bees and sold the honey to supermarkets throughout the city.

For years we'd had recurring problems with a swarm of bees that had found a home in the eaves of the roof above our bedroom. The area had been fumigated many times, but the bees always came back. They'd make a nuisance of themselves when it was hot by stinging the gardener and intimidating plumbers, electricians or anyone on the premises doing maintenance work. My mother had been allergic to bee stings, so I had great respect for them. I happened to mention the situation to Cheryl one day when she was ordering more honey labels.

"No problem at all," she said. "I remove swarms. If they're in an unreachable place, I'll have to destroy them. The secret is to paint the area afterwards with diesel. They hate the smell."

Cheryl arrived that evening in a large truck, with a long ladder and a capable assistant. The exercise didn't take long at all. I appreciated the fact that we weren't made to feel guilty about having to kill the bees.

Inevitably, we'd found ourselves discussing books. Cheryl had recently read a book by an Australian author, Sara Henderson. This woman, who ran a cattle ranch in the Australian outback, was extremely gutsy. She'd had to put up with a philandering husband, whose impractical schemes had contributed, in large measure, to their financial difficulties. Cheryl was fascinated both by the differences and the similarities to our way of life in Zimbabwe.

"One realises how vast Australia is when you read her accounts of getting from their ranch to the nearest city, Darwin," Cheryl said. "Civilisation was hundreds of kilometres away. And she and her children frequently had to fly in a light plane piloted by that tomcatting, irresponsible man."

Apart from Diana, who had recently been widowed and Glenda, who was divorced, Cheryl was the only single person in the Book Club. We assumed that she was either divorced or separated.

That October, it was Cheryl's turn to be our hostess. We could sense, when we arrived, however, that she was not herself. She seemed agitated and jumpy.

"Ladies," she said, "I might as well tell you straight away what happened to me yesterday. I had a visit from the police. They had a warrant and they spent four hours here searching the house."

We stared at her incredulously. "But whatever could they have been looking for?" asked Geraldine. "Foreign currency? Firearms? Subversive literature? MDC T-shirts?"

"The warrant said that they were looking for 'processed gold, unprocessed gold, precious minerals processed or not processed, offensive materials or substances'."

We were amazed. "Good grief," said Jeanette, "how awful! What did you do? Did you phone your lawyer?"

"They wouldn't let me use the phone," said Cheryl. "I was really scared. I insisted on having Dumisani with me. He helps me with the bees, as you know. There were four of them. It was intimidating, especially as I had no idea how they could possibly imagine that I was a gold dealer. I never wear jewellery. You'd think they'd be out looking for someone staggering under the weight of heavy gold chains."

"Please, Cheryl," I said. "Start from the beginning."

"Well," Cheryl began, "at about 8.45 yesterday morning I was ironing here in this room, when I heard someone at the gate. Dumisani called me and said that the police wanted to see me. The gate was locked, but two of them had climbed over it, which was scary. They handed me the warrant, and told me that they were going to search the house."

"Did you ask to see their IDs?" asked Jeanette.

"Yes, I did," replied Cheryl. "They took out their cards and showed them to me. Their photos were printed in colour and the IDs looked legit. But how many of us know what a police ID actually looks like? We're so vulnerable in a situation like this. It's not as if we live in Canada or the UK and can demand to have our rights and privacy respected."

We were imagining little Cheryl bristling with indignation, as four men loomed over her, trying to intimidate her. She would have been formidable, despite her size.

She went on to tell us that the warrant referred to 'the owner or occupant'. She rented the house and shared it with someone who used it occasionally as a base when he had to come into town. His section of the house was locked and there were no duplicate keys. The police seemed to find this an unusual and rather suspicious arrangement.

We were rather intrigued, and wondered whether this was a mysterious lover that she hadn't told us about.

"No," laughed Cheryl. "No, no! Not my type. We hardly even communicate with one another. He keeps to his part of the house when he's here, which isn't often. I never even know when he's coming. I just find him here, when I come back from wherever I've been. He's a very private person."

The police had started off in the laundry.

"One policeman searched, while another took notes. The other two just stood and watched me. You can imagine how unnerving it was. They pulled every article of dirty washing from the laundry basket and itemised it. They took every clean garment out of the washing machine and scrutinised it carefully. They unloaded the freezer and the fridge and looked in every plastic container, bottle and jar. When they got to the pantry, they suddenly got very excited." She paused.

"Why?" we all chorused.

"They found a little packet of thyme! 'What's this?' they asked. 'Do you smoke marijuana? I had to convince them that these were herbs I used to flavour meat.

The search went on and on. When they got to the linen cupboard, they pulled out my all my sheets, pillowcases and towels and dumped them on the floor. There were large, hard lumps of something secreted among the folds of the sheets. 'What's this?' they asked, looking at me triumphantly. I could see them thinking, 'Ha, guilty, as charged. Gold, at last. We're about to make an arrest.'

'Go ahead,' I said. 'Open them up.'

They did, and out fell several beautifully-wrapped cakes of Roger and Gallet soap. It's my favourite soap. I use one a year as a treat and put the others among my linen, because they make it smell fresh. How's that for a soap commercial?

They became hopeful, again, for a moment, when they discovered tiny white pills in the medicine cabinet in the bathroom. 'Drugs!' I could imagine them thinking. 'These are homeopathic pills,' I explained. Finally, when we got to my bedroom, their day was made. They found a locked gun cabinet and my fishing jacket in which I had a number of rounds of ammunition for a 308 rifle. I explained that I'd handed in the 308 to the Stops Camp armoury, as required by law. In my cupboard, however, was a Martini-Henry rifle.

'It's an antique - a collector's item, which has been rendered safe,' I told them.

'Where is the key for the gun cabinet?' they demanded of me. I don't have a key, as I don't keep anything of mine in there. It's Rob's stuff. I couldn't convince them that it had nothing to do with me (why was the gun cabinet in *my* bedroom, after all?) and that I couldn't get hold of Rob to get a key from him. So they decided to break the padlock. Naturally, they hadn't brought their own kit.

I had been frightened, but this made me angry and sarcastic. I provided them with a tyre lever and a hammer, and asked them why they didn't have their own tools. When they eventually broke the lock and got the safe open, they found a rifle and a revolver (with the appropriate licences), a Livingstone Mint Collection and a cash box full of photographs. There was nothing else.

All they had, then, that was even remotely interesting was my ammo. I insisted that each one of them signed for the rounds on the back of my copy of their search warrant. 'Why do you want all of us to sign?' they objected. 'Because one of you might get run down by a bus tonight, or someone might get transferred,' I responded tersely. By then I'd had enough of being harassed and hassled. They left just before lunch, instructing me to report to Hillside Police Station the next day to sort out the matter of the rounds they were holding.

In fact, I subsequently discovered that I was perfectly entitled to keep rounds at home since my weapon had been handed in to the armoury at Stops Camp. They gave them back to me first thing this morning when I went down there.

So there we have it, ladies. That was how I spent yesterday morning. I decided in the afternoon that I would set about space-clearing the house since there was so much negative energy about."

Cheryl had held our unwavering attention while she related her experiences with the police. Now she was talking about something called "space-clearing"...

"Have you heard of 'Feng shui'?" she asked.

Some of us had. It was an eastern concept that had something to do with where to build one's home and how to arrange the furniture in one's office. Our definitions were very vague. I knew that my sister believed that there was a lot to be said about "bad" and "good" Feng shui.

"Feng shui involves placing articles and furniture in such a way as to benefit one's whole being," Cheryl explained. "Placement would affect such aspects of one's life as prosperity, relationships, attitudes and travel. When you house clean in the normal way of things, you space-clear, too, by moving energy about. Energy can become clogged, and will manifest itself as a bad atmosphere, giving the occupier of the house a subtle sense that all is not well."

"My mum used to talk about being able 'to cut the atmosphere with a knife' when there was tension between my father and us three children," I said.

"Exactly," agreed Cheryl. "When the police left yesterday, it was migraine material. The energy throughout the house was distorted. The atmosphere was murky, and horribly unsettled. It was as if there were psychedelic lines merging and spiking. You know how you feel when you see a shirt or something with a design of thin stripes close together. You can't bear to look at it because it makes you feel nauseous and disoriented. That's what it was like.

You can use a bell, or you can simply clap or hum. You start with the corners from the bottom up. You work upwards three times systematically, and on the third occasion, you can actually hear that the sounds are different. You progress from there to the middle of the room and so on. Wind chimes also help to dispel negative forces as well as to activate ch'i in an area where it might be slow-moving. Ch'i is the life-giving breath or energy that shapes and animates all life. It's continually moving and changing – the places where it gathers produce positive energy. We need to tap into that 'electricity of life' and restore the harmony that has been displaced."

"Why is it," wondered Shirley aloud, "that most western men would totally discount this sort of thing as absolute rubbish? They would laugh at the gullibility of women, and change the subject to rugby, golf or cricket. Women, on the other hand, are prepared to listen and to consider the possibility that such a thing does actually exist."

"*'There are more things in heaven and earth, Horatio,*
Than are dreamt of in your philosophy...'" quoted Margaret softly.

Cheryl had a book called "The Feng Shui Work Book". During tea some of us browsed through it. I found myself glancing furtively into the corners of the room. Was the energy there settled now? If it were visible, would it look like a dragon or some other creature that one associated with Chinese mythology? I wondered what Nina (thousands of miles away in

Perth) would have said in response to such New Age ideas. As a devout and extremely conservative Catholic, she would have rejected them totally, I was sure. She would have said a decade of the rosary once the police had left.

Colleen would have dismissed the whole energy concept as 'crap' if she had been there.

SAFE HOME

"For the last year or so, as you know," said Colleen, "I've wanted to sell our house. Big houses with swimming pools are albatrosses for ageing couples like us. But Liam couldn't stand the idea of moving into Coronation Cottages or Garden Park with neighbours so close. You know what a private person he is."

Book Club was at Colleen's this Saturday. I'd arrived a little early so that we could chat. Her house held many memories for me. In the nineties, Colleen and Liam had been party animals, and their "hoolies" had lasted until the early hours of the morning. I recalled one memorable evening when a group of rather inebriated men decided to play "bok-bok" in the garden. This typically macho Zimbabwean "game" involves one of the two teams bending to present a long line of bodies. Each member of the opposing team takes a short run and leaps as far as possible to straddle the stooped figures. The question is will the receiving team collapse under the weight of their riders? Or will the jumpers fall off?

On this occasion there was no dispute. The spectators, who had been cheering on the jumpers from the veranda, heard a loud and frightening crack. A portly gentleman (no longer a young man in his prime) collapsed writhing in agony on the ground. His "rider" scrambled away hurriedly – too late, unfortunately. Their guest had broken his leg and had to be taken to hospital to have it set. The incident did cast a dampener on the party for a while. Then the more light-hearted began to recount stirring tales of other manly exploits.

These days, however, few people threw parties. Certainly not our age group anyway. They were too expensive and required too much effort. It didn't seem right, either, some like Stella felt, to spend money on riotous living, while people were starving.

Colleen laughed heartily when I reminded her of the bok-bok party. "Those were the good old days, weren't they?" she said wistfully.

I remembered several St Patrick's Day celebrations, when Liam and Colleen proudly wore their shamrocks. Irish people seldom, if ever, lost their identity, no matter how long they had lived away from "home". We would listen to plaintive Irish music, eat Irish stew and Colleen's delicious potato bread and drink potent Irish coffee. I recalled Colleen once making a special dessert for our boys involving green and orange jelly and custard.

When Larry listened to Irish music, he always quoted the lines:

"For the great Gaels of Ireland
Are the men that God made mad.
For all their wars are merry,
And all their songs are sad..."

"So we've decided to sell the house," said Colleen. "I finally got Liam to agree. We advertised in 'Morning Mirror' and were amazed at the response we got. We were inundated with queries. But I found that I had to insist on doing the guided tours myself. Liam kept telling potential buyers about the drawbacks and the negatives. I had to hide him away while I did the negotiating. He needs to go on one of the courses you do for your reps on selling skills.

Anyway, we got a firm offer almost immediately – a very good one – and we've accepted it. I can't tell you how relieved I feel. The new owners – black, of course – are allowing us to lease the house from them for the next few months while we decide what we want to do. They're also going to take most of the furniture. So I don't have to worry about selling that either. I'll take the bits and pieces they don't want to the auctions. Special things I'll give to the kids. We'll just be left with a couple of suitcases of clothes. That's all we need. We want to travel light. As you get older, possessions don't mean much. The only thing that's important is peace of mind."

This was a very different Colleen. She was positively brimming with joy and gratitude at their good fortune. They certainly deserved a lucky break. Several robberies in recent years had made them feel vulnerable and insecure. Liam's truck, Colleen's Peugeot, and their trailer had been stolen in the latest of these, along with Liam's golf clubs and all their camping equipment. This, in spite of 6ft walls with razor wire and chained, padlocked gates. Both vehicles had been fitted with cut-off switches. Both had been locked and alarmed.

The others had begun to arrive. Everyone immediately noticed the difference in our hostess.

Colleen was teaching "Great Expectations" to her O level English class. She loved Dickens.

"So often I think that we should re-read the classics," she said. "Few modern writers can compete with Dickens, the Brontë sisters and Jane Austen. Listen to this... many of you will remember the opening chapter of 'Great Expectations'..."

There was magic in her voice as she read aloud the famous words:

"'Ours was the marsh country, down by the river, within, as the river wound, twenty miles of the sea. My first most vivid and broad impression of the identity of things, seems to me to have been gained on a memorable raw afternoon towards evening. At such a time I found out for certain, that this bleak place overgrown was the churchyard.... And that the dark flat wilderness beyond the churchyard, intersected with dykes and mounds and gates, with scattered cattle feeding on it was the marshes; and that the low leaden line beyond, was the river; and that the distant savage lair from which the wind was rushing was the sea; and that the small bundle of shivers growing afraid of it all and beginning to cry, was Pip...'"

We could see Magwitch, a fearsome figure, rising up suddenly and dramatically from among the graves to pounce on Pip. We breathed in the cold, dank air and felt Pip's terror.

She was right. Few books began in so arresting a manner.

Everyone was delighted to hear her news about the house.

"What are your plans, Colleen? Where will you go? Will you leave Zim?" asked Mary.

"We've talked about little else for weeks now," said Colleen. "I've decided to hand in my notice at the end of this term. I'll take my classes through to exams in November, and then I'll wind down. I've finished with teaching. Liam and I are thinking about taking what we're calling 'a geriatric gap-year'. We would spend time in Harare with Paul, Felicity and our two darling grandchildren. Their baby girl is six months old tomorrow. Then we'd go to Durban and stay a while with my sister-in-law. After a couple of months by the sea, we'd fly off to Canada to stay with Brendan and then spend a few months with my sister in America. She's so much better, thank God. And 'fall' in the States is beautiful. It's a wonderful time of year to visit."

The idea of a geriatric gap-year was an amusing concept. Quite often school leavers took off for a 'gap-year' when they were unsure of what to do next. Their parents would buy them return tickets and send them to the UK where they would find temporary jobs and travel as widely as possible. This gave them a clearer picture as to choice of career. That was the theory, anyway! Their parents fondly imagined that they'd go on to university having got wanderlust and frivolousness out of their systems.

"And after that?" asked Cheryl.

"After that, we'll go back to Ireland. Don't know where yet."

When everyone else had gone, Colleen asked me quietly to stay on for a while.

"Have you heard of 'Safe-Home Ireland'?" she asked.

"No," I replied, intrigued.

"A few months ago, Charlotte and Francis, emailed us urging us to consider returning to Ireland. *They* hadn't wanted to leave Zim, but felt that they had no ties here any longer. Their children had grown up, married and settled overseas. They returned to County Armagh six years ago, and have never looked back. Charlotte told me of a couple of websites that offered elderly Irish people living abroad sheltered housing if they chose to come home.

"I began a correspondence with someone at Safe-Home Ireland, strangely enough someone with the same name as mine. She knows all about what is happening here, as they have had a number of applications from Irish Zimbabweans. We qualify for repatriation. They'll find us a home and we can apply for pensions. They say that in recent years the Irish Government has begun to recognise the role emigrants played in creating the conditions that made the Celtic Tiger possible.

Can you imagine what this welcoming and accepting attitude has done for our morale? For years now, we've known that whites like us are second-class citizens in Zim, in spite of all the years we have given to this country. Ireland *wants* us back! There's no penalty for leaving. They *want* us back and are actually prepared to look after us when we get there."

Colleen burst into tears. I couldn't help shedding a few myself.

This was a fairy-tale ending for them – a solution at last to their problems.

And for Larry and me...something to think about...

FIRST RAINS

The Wilderness Safari Lodge on Jeanette's Farm in the Nyamandhlovu area was a green oasis of luxuriant lawns, shady trees and tropical plants. Jeanette and Geraldine had driven us out to the farm in their SUVs for Book Club and lunch afterwards. We'd travelled along the Victoria Falls Road, past kilometre after kilometre of bare earth peppered with huts and very little else but the inevitable chickens and goats. Gone were the crops in the irrigated lands we used to see. Almost all the farms in this district had been invaded or taken over at various stages of the land "acquisition" programme.

Jeanette and Julian were still on theirs, after years of uncertainty. Jeanette wasn't able to give a logical explanation as to why they had been luckier than most. "One has to live a day at a time," she said. "We could be given an eviction notice tomorrow or next month. Who knows? Just recently, we've been having altercations with a black farmer about keeping his chickens too close to our ostriches. He's an unpleasant character, who refuses to listen to reason. He's just being provocative. But the close proximity of other livestock to ostriches contravenes certain regulations that have to be observed in order for us to export to world markets. It's a worry."

We drove past Andrew and Rita Hoskins's farm where, some years previously, a siege had been mounted at the height of the farm invasions. Andrew and Rita had refused to leave their farm and had locked themselves into the homestead. Rabid hordes of chanting war veterans with axes and all manner of primitive weapons had tried to intimidate them. The Vic Falls Road had been lined with vehicles belonging to farmers from the area and friends from Bulawayo (among them Larry and Terry), who were there to support them and to provide a tacit warning to the war vets. This group, which was in telephone contact with Andrew and Rita, hoped that its presence would help to defuse a terrifyingly volatile situation. Everyone knew that there would be no police back up, as this would conveniently be viewed as a "political" situation – one in which the police would not intervene. Eventually, the Hoskins had to leave, as the outcome was inevitable. Greed would prevail. Their farm had been one of the best in the area, yielding excellent harvests of paprika and ostriches.

Moira, Mary and I had attended an interdenominational church service at St Mary's Cathedral some months after this particular farm invasion. Various victims of intimidation and torture had been invited to give their testimonies during the service. Among these was a young woman who had worked on Utopia Farm. She wept as she described what she and the other farm labourers had lost. They had lost everything. Their homes, their jobs, their opportunity to educate their children at the farm school and the medical facilities that Rita provided free of charge. This young woman had worked with the ostriches and had been proud of the healthy birds under her care. Those who had taken over the farm knew nothing of farming, and were not interested in providing for the farm workers. It was a moving testimony because she was articulate and sincere, and because Andrew and Rita were in the congregation weeping, too.

The road through Jeanette and Julian's property took us past pens housing hundreds of ostriches, which, like the Hoskins's, were very valuable birds, as sale of their meat, skins and feathers brought vital foreign currency into the country. These creatures had a reputation for viciousness, however. We'd all heard stories of people being seriously injured or even kicked to death by ostriches. They were not particularly attractive birds, either, with their long legs and necks and feather duster tails. They didn't inspire the "oh, sweet... how fluffy, cuddly, cute" emotions that so many baby animals and birds do. One might be tempted to hug an adorable baby elephant or lion cub, but certainly not an ungainly ostrich chick.

From the viewing platform in front of the main lodge building, we could see kudu and warthog gathering to drink. What a lovely setting for Book Club on this very hot November day, when the country was parched and desperate for rain. We settled into comfortable armchairs in Jeanette's lounge with tall glasses of iced tea, and, for a few moments, reviewed the situation in Book Club itself, before we moved on to discuss what we had read during the month.

Three of our members would be leaving after Christmas. The political and economic climate had deteriorated to such an extent that, once again, many were being forced to consider alternative options.

Glenda was very tense and pale. She'd always had a lovely figure, but was beginning to look too thin. Born and brought up in Zimbabwe, she was obviously taking a great deal of strain, as she was leaving her entire life and history behind. She was close to her father, in particular, and Australia was thousands of kilometres away.

She was taking up a teaching position at a school in Perth.

Diana was returning to England. She was glad to be going. Unlike Colleen and Liam, there were no grandchildren in the equation, which had made *their* decision to leave so much more difficult and painful. She relished the thought of being in a First World country. She was tired of having to scrounge for every litre of fuel, no easy task for a woman alone. It would be wonderful to go shopping for groceries, and not to be shocked at how prices had escalated during the course of a week. It would be marvellous to live normally again. She had always loved city life and was looking forward to being with Andrea, her daughter, again.

Colleen and Liam were both Catholics from Belfast. But they had no desire to return to Northern Ireland. Not with Ian Paisley soon to be installed as First Minister. There was a cottage ready for them in a little village near the famous Knock Shrine.

They were in Durban enjoying the sea and the sunshine, before leaving for the winter in County Mayo. They'd decided against travelling after all. They wanted to settle as soon as possible in a comfortable and stable First World environment.

"My best read," said Diana, "was Margaret Forster's 'Daphne du Maurier', a biography so good, that it read like a novel. I endorse 'The Daily Mail' critic's comment on the back cover that the book was as gripping as 'Rebecca'.

"I was delighted to find the latest Elizabeth George 'With No One as Witness' in Perth, when I was there for my interview," Glenda said. "We've all been fans of Elizabeth George for years and have loved Inspector Lynley. If we were forced to choose between them, I know that Margaret would opt for Harry Bosch, but I think I'd go for the Inspector! You'll all be pleased to hear that Barbara Havers plays a major role in this story. A serial killer is on the loose. Lynley, Barbara and Winston Nkata are called upon to investigate a bizarre series of child murders. Lynley suffers a shocking tragedy, and is forced to make a decision that will haunt him for the rest of his life. For once it seems that Barbara might find happiness. Definitely Elizabeth George at her best, keeping the reader guessing."

"Has anyone seen the TV series?" asked Diana. "Barbara Havers is positively glamorous, and completely unrealistic. Why must they spoil the characterisation? She adds such spice to the stories and is a perfect foil for debonair Lynley."

"'The Kite Runner' is my rave," said Shirley, "and the best book I've read this year. Khaled Hosseini is new to all of us. The story is set in Afghanistan, and we learn about the old, rich, fascinating Afghan culture. The author's descriptions of the kite-flying contests in which he participated very successfully as a child are most interesting. We move on to read of the horror of the Russian occupation and then, even worse, of the tyranny of the Taliban. There is a graphic description of a woman being stoned to death for committing adultery. People assemble to watch the gruesome spectacle as if it were some kind of sporting event. The story is beautiful, though. Those of you who haven't read it yet have a real treat in store."

"We're extremely lucky to be in this Book Club," said Jeanette. "In so many of the other Book Clubs, they just chat, choose books and have coffee and wine afterwards. There's no question of reviewing books. This Book Club encourages us to broaden our reading tastes and to learn about different authors whose books we've never read. Many of us might have been put off by a book by an Afghan. We would, perhaps, have regarded him as an abuser of women in the Taliban mould, without giving him a chance. Now we're all dying to read it."

Mary, Margaret and I had read Anita Shreve's "A Wedding in December".

"Definitely not her best," said Mary. "I think all her novels are superbly researched and make fascinating reading. This is a good read, but not up to the standard of some of her earlier works. And just look at the cover. Hardly the body of someone in her forties."

Mary had always said that Anita Shreve was her favourite contemporary female author. Her books had never particularly impressed me before. It was difficult to say why, exactly. I thought it was probably because, in my opinion, her plots were sometimes implausible and contrived. But I had really enjoyed this one.

In "A Wedding in December" Anita Shreve explores a series of very complex relationships. Bill has left his wife and children to marry Bridget. They had been lovers at college. Bridget has breast cancer and has just finished a course of chemotherapy, which has left her exhausted and often ill.

"This is the real versus the ideal, isn't it?" said Mary. "Marriage is something that has to be worked at. It's a serious commitment. You can't just ditch your wife and children because you've met up again with the person you *used to* love. One's wife and children do not deserve to be shrugged off in this casual fashion. Such behaviour is grossly irresponsible."

"I thought it was very good," said Margaret. "Much better than 'Light on Snow'."

Every month, exciting books made their way into Book Club. These came from outside the country. New books were no longer available in Zimbabwe. The husbands would obligingly bring books back from business trips along with the usual tins of tuna, bottles of Bovril and tubes of toothpaste. Relatives and friends would bring books as gifts whenever they visited.

"Two fascinating 'reads'," said Geraldine, "are 'My Sister's Keeper' by Jodi Picoult and 'Sickened: The True Story of a Lost Childhood' by Julie Gregory. The first tells the tale of a child conceived so that she can donate stem cells to her elder sister who has leukaemia. This thirteen-year-old hires a lawyer, when her mother attempts to coerce her into giving up one of her kidneys. The second, 'Sickened', is about Munchausen's by Proxy, a disease that has been called the world's most hidden and, therefore, most dangerous form of child abuse."

Book Club drifted into a delicious lunch. Afterwards, as we sipped our coffee, large drops of rain began to pelt the plants on the wooden viewing platform. This was the first rain of the season, a most welcome relief, after the intense, wilting heat we'd been subjected to for months. We crowded to the door to watch and to smell the rain at closer quarters.

Perhaps this would mean the beginning of inflow to the dams and an end to Bulawayo's water problems. Many households had been without a regular supply of water for months on end and electricity cuts were frequent. It was a relief to come home after work on a Friday to find that the City Council had sourced enough fuel to remove three weeks' accumulation of refuse. It was a relief to turn on a tap first thing in the morning and watch clean, clear water running out. So often these days, if water came out of the taps at all, it was either a dark, undrinkable muddy brown or a cloudy white liquid that looked as though the City Council had decided to dose us all with disprin.

We could take nothing for granted any more.

YEAR-END

15 December

I hate leaving the factory at this time of year.
What if one of the workers mixes the wrong shade of ink?
Or uses the small block on the A4 diaries instead of the large
one? Or if a production schedule needs to be changed, because
someone is threatening to cancel his order? If I'm on the spot,
I might be able to persuade Reg at our lithographic printers to
run our desk planners next instead of the National Railways'
calendar.

I usually enjoy catching up with Cynthia and the Harare
reps. But not in December. And not for a Christmas lunch.
They'd probably prefer me to be at the factory supervising their
customers' deliveries, anyway. Then they wouldn't have to field
so many queries.

16 December

Sinking gently through troughs of air, we slipped closer
towards Bulawayo. Some of the passengers were dozing. Others
chatted quietly. Although the cabin lights had been switched off,
dim beams from overhead consoles lit books and magazines.

Larry and I had enjoyed our day in Harare. We'd had an
excellent lunch at a new restaurant in the city centre. The reps
had been in good form, and it had been easy to ignore our
problems for a while.

I leaned towards the tiny, grubby window. The lights of
the city were clearer now, sparkling jewels strung through the
darkness. We edged closer, gliding and dipping, and then the
runway beacons stretched out ahead, beckoning us towards the
final descent.

We felt a surge of relief as the plane bumped wearily onto the
tarmac, gradually slowed and then taxied round to come to a
halt in front of the unfinished airport building. We remembered
to bow our heads to avoid the low doorway, picked our way

gingerly down the rickety steps and stumbled thankfully onto the bus waiting to take us round to the hangar that for years had served as the "temporary" terminal.

As we drove through Queen's Park on the outskirts of town, jagged bolts of lightning ripped the sky apart. The storm pounced on the line of homebound cars, raking our windscreens with great gusts of swirling rain. In menacing barrages, thunder crashed violently overhead.

We could see nothing of the road now. As the sheets of rain slammed into us, the long line of vehicles slowed to a crawl. There were no streetlights to assist us – obviously the power to this area had been cut off. As we made our way through the suburb, cars ahead of us stalled in the downpour. We were thankful that we were driving a twin cab with a high clearance.

We turned off Robert Mugabe Way towards Paddonhurst, still travelling at a snail's pace. Here, too there were no streetlights. We knew we were close to the shopping centre when we came suddenly upon the warning humps. We struggled on, eventually reaching the Harare Road. We couldn't use the left lane, as a number of cars pulled over on the verge appeared to be stuck in the pooling water. Some had only one headlight that worked. Others had no lights at all and no reflectors and were a serious hazard to fellow road-users. The potholes on this major thoroughfare were really dangerous, too. If we were to hit one of the very deep ones, now filled with rainwater and obscured by the blinding rain, we could wreck our suspension or damage an axle.

The glare of oncoming headlights was blinding in spite of the rain gusting down. Like everyone else, we had our lights on "bright". There was no option. It was the only way to determine which side of the road we were on. We needed to turn right into George Avenue, if we could find it in this crazy world of battering rain and intermittent dazzling brightness.

Our truck shuddered as heavy city-bound vehicles surged by, uncomfortably close. We hoped that one of these might point the way to George Avenue, since there was no longer a sign there to indicate the intersection. Then, for a fleeting second, the lights of a massive pantechnicon illuminated the pole of a streetlight to the right, and, with a sigh of relief, Larry turned quickly off the Harare Road.

The rain began to ease slightly, just enough for us to see the bags and bins of uncollected refuse littering the streets of Kumalo. Each Friday we put our rubbish out to be collected. Each Saturday morning, we retrieved it. After six weeks, municipal trucks still hadn't collected our garbage. Perhaps the rivers rushing down the street would wash it away, relieving us of the problem.

We drove up to our front door, grabbed our briefcases and jumped out of the truck. In those few seconds we were drenched. We found the right key and let ourselves into our warm, dry house. Carefully, we felt our way along the passage and into the kitchen where we kept the candles and matches. The heads came off the first three matches we struck, but the fourth match flared brightly.

We changed into our dressing gowns and opened a bottle of wine.

It had been a long day.

Part VI

SUFFERING THAT VERY LITTLE INCONVENIENCE

JANUARY 2006 - MARCH 2007

New Members

There were only seven of us at the January Book Club at Shirley's house. Glenda was already in Perth and Diana in England. Colleen and Liam were still with their relatives in Durban.

Shirley had just read the new Anita Shreve. She thought the section describing Bridget's illness was particularly well-handled.

"I think I may have come over as being a bit of a pain last month," Mary said. "Perhaps I was being too idealistic in taking the moral high ground. 'Successful' personalities and 'happy' relationships are certainly not always the way they seem. It makes me think about the 'face' that each of us wears – the image we want to project. Who can tell what is going on in another's mind and what a person is really like?"

"Absolutely fascinating," agreed Margaret. The smaller group was much easier for her to cope with. She could concentrate better on what each person was saying, and fewer women made less noise. She could hear most of what was being said, especially when the speaker remembered to look at her directly and speak clearly.

"Do you remember that popular series of books we read years ago?" I asked. "The first was called 'Glittering Images'. The author, Susan Howatch, believes that we all wear a mask or 'image', beneath which seethe conflicting, dark emotions that others are completely unaware of."

"Yes," said Shirley. "A man may be one personality when he is with his wife and quite another in the pub. No wonder so many marriages are in trouble."

Shirley's husband, James, was a keen gardener. Their narrow, tree-lined driveway wound up a hill through lush green lawns. (They had an excellent borehole.) He'd designed water features around which grew feathery pampas grass and tall bamboos, and had positioned metal sculptures of squat guinea fowl and long-legged herons among the ornamental grasses. Their lounge looked out onto a small swimming pool surrounded by bougainvillea shrubs covered in bright pink, purple and orange flowers. Did they work in their garden together? I didn't think so. Their interests seemed very different. Shirley was essentially an in-doors person.

"I often wonder how my children view me," said Mary. "Do they see me merely as a mother without my own identity? Do they even consider that there is a part of me that has nothing to do with them or with the family unit? For some years now, I've been keeping a journal in which I've recorded my feelings and reactions to situations and events. They can read it one day, if ever they want to learn who I really am."

"What a brilliant idea," Margaret said enthusiastically. "The only problem is that they're boys. Introspection seems to appeal to girls more than it does to boys. Margaret Forster writes so revealingly about family dynamics."

"Yes," said Shirley. "I'm not sure that men know the meaning of the word or understand the concept. I've got used to knee-jerk responses from my lot."

"I only came to know my father during the last three years of his life," Mary went on, warming to her subject. "While my mother was alive, he was the character she wanted him to be. He took on a persona that wasn't his own. Prior to my mother's death, if I telephoned them and he answered the phone, he would say 'hello' and hand me over to her. They both assumed that I wanted to speak to *her*, and that he and I had nothing to say to one another. Afterwards, my mother would relay those aspects of our conversation she considered to be of interest to him."

Jeanette had read 'Sickened' by Julie Gregory. "This is a horrifying story, first reviewed by Geraldine in November at my book club out at the farm. It's a book that you all must read. Depressing but compelling, it is almost impossible to imagine that a mother could attempt to inflict open-heart surgery on her healthy child.

The foreword to her book is written by a doctor from the University of Alabama. He comments on Munchausen's by Proxy as follows: '.... (It) may be the single most complex – and lethal – form of maltreatment known today. It is formally defined as the falsification or induction of physical and/or emotional illness by a caretaker of a dependent person. In most cases, the perpetrator is a mother and the victim is her own child'. The doctors' and nurses' behaviour is appalling and culpable. Why didn't they question and investigate before taking the mother's word that the child was ill?"

Stella looked thoughtful.

"Many years ago, when I was a very young nurse on night duty, a patient in her thirties told me that she was in a bad way. She begged me to give her some strong painkillers. As you know, nurses can't simply dish out drugs on request. Certainly not a junior nurse, anyway. Instead of feeling compassion and concern, as I would normally have done, I felt a sharp stab of suspicion. I sensed something strange and out of sync, because I couldn't see pain in her face. In fact, she was very attractive and looked the picture of health."

"How could you be sure whether or not someone was 'in pain'?" asked Jeanette rather impatiently. "Is it evident from a person's expression or would you see 'pain' in the eyes?"

Jeanette was a sceptic. Things were either white or they were black. There were no shades of grey.

Stella considered the question seriously for a moment. She found Jeanette rather daunting.

"In both, probably. But most strongly, I think in the mouth and cheeks. It's quite difficult to define. If you are used to being around sick people, then you just know..."

She resumed her story.

"Later that night, when the woman's doctor was doing his rounds of the surgical wards, I told him that she had asked for pain-killers. Her chart indicated that only two or three paracetamol had been prescribed and that she had been given these earlier in the evening. I was a bit nervous to express an opinion, but I mentioned to him that she didn't really seem to be in pain. He looked at me closely. I had the feeling that he was noticing me as a person for the first time. I wasn't just an unimportant, inexperienced junior nurse.

'Well done, nurse,' he said. 'She has Munchausen's. She's had a hysterectomy and two bowel ops and tomorrow she is to have her second back operation. She has been in and out of hospital for years. She's a professional patient, who demands attention by pretending to be ill. There isn't a thing wrong with her. She's as healthy as you or me.'"

"I was shocked," Stella went on. "How could he keep operating on someone who had absolutely nothing wrong with her? He must have known what I was thinking."

'If *I* don't 'operate' on her, then someone else will,' he said. 'And that *someone else* might not be as good a surgeon as me. I'll just open her up and close her again until the next time.'

"He left me feeling rather queasy. She had her back 'operation' the following day. That was my one and only experience of Munchausen's. I haven't thought about it for years."

Mary had bought a new book about the Boer War and about life in a concentration camp. The Boer women and children had suffered terribly. She described how the British soldiers had torched the farmers' buildings and crops and laid waste the surrounding farm land. They had also massacred their livestock. In an incongruous display of mastery, they would make the Boer wife play hymns on the piano (it seemed that every family owned a piano), while they burned their victims' furniture and possessions. Then the piano would be dragged outside and an axe put through it as a final symbolic gesture.

Jeanette had read widely on this subject, and agreed that the Boer women and children had been atrociously treated, and that the "Brits" had a great deal to answer for. She, personally, would never forgive them for the way they'd "ditched" Rhodesia.

We were always amused when she castigated the "Brits", since she was the epitome of a cultured Englishwoman. I could imagine her in tweeds and brogues serving tea and cucumber sandwiches to guests at their lodge on the farm. When she first joined Book Club, we'd wondered whether she was a snob. As we'd got to know her better, we'd realised that she was very honest and always spoke her mind.

After the reviews, we considered the type of person we needed to replace those who had left. This was always a controversial topic. Shirley felt new members should be young and that we should recruit ladies from Mary's age group. I felt that suitability rather than youth was the key consideration. We had to be selective, as the wrong people could alter the tone and focus of our little group. Although there were only a few of us left from the original book club, we remembered clearly how different expectations and attitudes could change the atmosphere completely.

As usual, we were unable to agree.

MIGRATING SWALLOWS

30 January

Zimbabwean drivers have become expert at dodging potholes. We veer about frenetically, trying to protect our precious cars from disintegrating completely. So preoccupied are we looking for pools of water concealing craters, that we are in danger of forgetting the antics of the driver on the opposite side, equally intent on negotiating his own set of hazards.

These days (according to our accountant), you can tell that a person is drunk if you see him driving in a straight line.

The short cut Sean and I took to How Mine was more a case of potholes concealing a road. We passed through the security boom at the mine entrance and headed down the hill to a eucalyptus plantation alongside the river. Sean said that it would be dusk before the swallows flew in to roost. He'd been there three weeks earlier with friends and knew what to expect.

We greeted friendly miners and their families as they passed by on their way to the mine compound. They were obviously used to seeing nature-lovers with binoculars and cameras at this time of year.

As the sky gradually darkened, we became aware of many small specks above us. At first, they seemed to have formed a holding pattern like aeroplanes circling above a busy airport waiting for permission from their flight controllers to come in to land. Then, gradually, they began to descend. I noticed bigger birds circling lazily among them. These, Sean said, were predators such as eagles, hawks and kites, there to pick off as many as took their fancy.

The swallows flew closer and closer, sweeping downwards in a mounting crescendo of excited sound. Suddenly, they were all around us. They settled in vast flocks, every bird choosing its own twig or spot on a branch.

Each group descended in a wave of swirling movement several minutes apart. The distant dots became larger and larger and then the next massive flock flooded in, racing towards us. Some came hurtling up the road, low and fast like laser-guided missiles in a science fiction movie, twisting and turning with pinpoint accuracy.

They all chose the trees by the river, ignoring the plantation on the opposite side of the road. A large raptor nearby lazily scanned the laden branches. After a few moments, it swooped casually down, snatched up a swallow and took off into the darkening evening.

We didn't take a short cut on the way back. Potholes during the day are bad enough, but at night, it's impossible to avoid all of them.

When we got home, we googled the migration habits of swallows.

The How Mine birds are British swallows, here for the winter. They fly at low altitudes and cover about 300 km each day. They feed entirely on flying insects, snapping up their food on the wing. At night they roost in huge flocks in reed beds at traditional stopover spots. Swallows return to the UK in April and May to breed in open countryside, often near water. By early September, having raised their young, most are preparing again to migrate.

2 February

It's going to be a very difficult year.

We've said the same thing every year since the farm invasions, of course.

There are very few commercial farmers left to benefit from the wonderful rains we've had. Fat Cats, who "own" formerly productive farms, visit their country homes for the occasional weekend in their Pajeros and Mercedes Benzes. They lounge on the cool colonial-style verandas with their young mistresses, drinking double whiskies. They don't plant crops. They've no idea how to farm, and no inclination to learn. Farm schools and clinics don't exist anymore. They're now relics of a past era.

There's no maize meal in the shops. Even the black market, which usually offers scarce commodities at exorbitant prices, hasn't been able to secure any. Rice, beans and pasta are available at a price, but they're no substitute for sadza[19], even if the people could afford them. Those of us who own businesses try to "make a plan" to source food for our employees.

This is why so many of us whites consider the indigenous people to be strangely submissive. Do they lack initiative? Where is their sense of outrage? Why are their expectations so low?

Last Monday the charming man who delivers lunch every day for our workers told me that he no longer looks forward to the weekend, because nothing nice ever happens. Christmas was dreary, and he was glad when it was over.

"We are suffering!" he said sadly. "What is going to happen to us?"

"What is the use of complaining?" he normally remarks with a wry grin, in response to our polite enquiries. "No-one listens!"

(This very English cliché always sounds incongruous coming from him.)

13 February

"What is going to happen to us?"

A few months ago, I could have said that at least we had a viable, active, principled opposition, concerned about the welfare of the people.

I could have said that the MDC was still our best hope for the future.

I could have said that it had remained true to its policy of non-violence in spite of the stolen elections and the horrors its MPs and supporters had suffered.

I could have said that, although its leaders had proved to be disappointing and even feeble, at least they had not attempted to grasp power and wealth for themselves.

I can no longer say this.

---

19 Sadza is a thickened porridge made from white maize (mealie-meal). It is the chief source of carbohydrate and the most popular meal for indigenous people.

Last October we were devastated to learn that there had been a split in the party, ostensibly over the issue of whether or not to field candidates for the senate. Many felt that Morgan Tsvangirai's powerful "kitchen cabinet", advisors and bodyguards were too influential. Some of these inner circle "officials" had violently assaulted fellow party members who were "out of line".

Had the MDC leader mutated into Napoleon, chief pig from "Animal Farm", and were his vicious dogs going to be used against his own followers? Did Morgan have the same faults and the same delusions of grandeur as the man he had sworn to displace?

And then – just to muddy the waters further – an Ndebele faction within the party emerged. This faction, led by the MDC's Secretary General, Professor Welshman Ncube and Vice President, Gibson Sibanda, spoke of disciplining Tsvangirai and of demanding his resignation. The feuding groups accused one another of wrongdoing. Tsvangirai's faction alleged that a senior party official from the opposing faction had misappropriated a substantial amount of foreign currency. There were also allegations that farms had been acquired.

David Coltart refused to align himself with either division. He wanted a reconciliation and order and sanity restored. At a public meeting he announced that he had committed himself to trying to bring this about.

After what the MDC and its loyal supporters have been through, the fragmentation of the party is heart-breaking and demoralising. Will all the effort and all the sacrifices be for nothing?

This is a betrayal of the people's trust. It's a betrayal of its vision - "a new Zimbabwe, a new beginning".

Can ZANU PF and the CIO have infiltrated the MDC and engineered the split?

Whatever the case, the MDC's credibility lies in tatters.

We have taken a giant step backward.

THE BEND-OVER BAZAAR

"Do you mean to tell me that you've never been to the "Bend-over Bazaar?" asked Cheryl.

I'd just admired the blouse she'd bought at the Revenue Hall flea market.

The Murambatsvina tsunami had swept the informal traders away the previous June. They'd been back for some months, however, earning a precarious living. It was quite possible that another tidal wave could obliterate their means of earning a living a second time, if the urban poor needed to be taught a further lesson. They were living on the edge.

Bulawayo's Revenue Hall is an imposing building with massive windows of copper-coloured one-way glass guaranteeing privacy to those who worked inside. I hadn't been there for years, and had forgotten what an impressive part of the town this was.

Cheryl had decided to introduce me to a very different type of shopping.

"Hang your bag round your neck," she said, "leaving both hands free. That way you'll be able to sort through piles of clothing more easily."

I paused at the top of the steps. There were hundreds of traders operating "stalls". Since there were no obvious demarcations, there must have been a series of unwritten rules. Some goods were arranged in neat rows on blankets. Here and there, at the more sophisticated stands, makeshift rails were being used to display garments. Crowds of browsers were digging through heaps of crumpled clothing that had been dumped unceremoniously on the concrete.

Most clothes were second-hand, Cheryl explained. One needed to be careful when considering an item.

"Watch out for missing buttons, frayed cuffs and stains," she cautioned. "Many of the marks will come out after a few washes, though. You'd need to use plenty of Preen."

It was a lovely morning. Not too hot, overcast without threatening rain, perfect for wandering about, unencumbered by time constraints. Many of the stalls displayed attractive garments unavailable in Zimbabwean shops. Little pleated denim skirts with tiny embroidered denim tops and tee shirts with colourful cowboy motifs made me wish I had grandchildren to buy gifts for.

I was hoping to find a couple of blouses for myself. Someone had commented the day before that I always wore blue. So definitely not blue. We found a rust-coloured top that cost only $250,000. A little better that buying something similar at Meikles or Edgars for $2,500,000. And no stains or missing buttons. The Revenue Hall windows provided excellent full-length mirrors, perfect for checking the fit and style of a garment. The shoppers, as they twisted and turned, critically considering potential outfits, must have been a source of great hilarity for the office workers within.

We came across friends and acquaintances, many of whom were sifting through the same piles of assorted clothing. Everyone seemed happy and relaxed - a pleasant change from the more stressed atmosphere of the city during the week. I was tempted to buy a denim shirt with Peanuts characters embroidered on the front pockets. There were a number of marks on it, though, so I decided not to put my tin of Preen to the test. Cheryl chose a brightly checked long-sleeved shirt for herself.

Here and there, youths sprawled on mattresses of clothes. No one appeared concerned that the loungers might be obscuring something the shoppers might fancy. If you wanted to sleep, well, you went ahead and slept. If you wanted to eat a roasted mealie while conducting a sale, that was perfectly natural and acceptable.

Like crows, we were drawn to those blankets where glittering costume jewellery and brightly coloured shoes with purple, yellow and blue flower designs were displayed. There were gorgeous brand-new black and white tops with spaghetti straps, decorated with sequinned butterflies and dragonflies. How marvellous it would be to be young again, to have firm upper arms without flab, a shapely chest without liver spots and a flat stomach with a sparkling belly ring. Even a couple of tattoos, perhaps?

We sat on the wall for a while, chatting. Cheryl had a slight cold and sore throat. She was dosing herself with a mixture of propolis, honey and lemon juice. Propolis, she explained, was a substance that bees used in their hives as a disinfectant and anti-biotic.

"I remember hearing a story from a colleague about a bee removal that took place in a tobacco barn," she told me. "The team carrying out the exercise found an adult owl and her eggs completely embalmed. The bees had obviously objected to the owl's being there, had stung her to death and then coated her with propolis. This prevented her from rotting and spoiling their honey."

I was fascinated and asked Cheryl whether she had read "The Secret Life of Bees" by Sue Monk Kidd. Cheryl hadn't been in Book Club at that time, but she owned a copy of the book. She, too, had loved it.

"I cannot comprehend the cruelty of people," she mused. "What is wrong with mankind that people are so caught up with their own egos? How can a father blame his daughter for his wife leaving him? A child, who was four years old at the time? It's pathetic that children try so desperately hard to please their parents in the hope of receiving affection and recognition from them. How often do parents praise their kids and communicate effectively with them? They should spend more time with their children and fewer hours in front of their television sets."

We remembered how Lily, the fourteen-year-old heroine in "The Secret Life of Bees" had yearned for her father's love and acceptance. She missed her mother dreadfully. She ran away with her father's black domestic worker, Rosaleen, and found sanctuary in the home of three black sisters, who kept bees. The story was set against a background of racial tension in 1964, when black Americans, led by Martin Luther King, were agitating for their civil rights.

August Boatwright took in the two runaways, provided the love and acceptance that Lily craved, and taught the young girl her own unique brand of spirituality. She, her sisters and their circle of friends believed that The Black Madonna had been instrumental in freeing their enslaved ancestors. Although their form of worship was highly unorthodox, it was about love, compassion and gratitude. Lily became August's apprentice and learned how to keep bees.

"Their spirituality was splendid," said Cheryl. "They saw the world in a wonderful, very simple way. August taught Lily the life-skills that she needed, in order to cope both practically and emotionally. I often wonder whether people write books to wake their readers up. Perhaps much of what they write about actually happened to them in one form or another, and is aimed at their own parents."

"Have you read 'To Kill a Mockingbird'?" I asked her. "It's one of my favourite books. I loved teaching it as an O Level set work. There was so much to discuss. I've never been able to find another book by Harper Lee. Yet it was a Pulitzer Prize winner and sold over 30,000,000 copies. The mockingbird in the story is a black man falsely charged with the rape of a white girl. It's set in the Deep South of the 1930s in a small town steeped in the prejudice of the time."

Cheryl hadn't read it, so there was a treat in store for her.

The crowd had increased in size. Children played games among the stalls, while their mothers chatted and lingered over potential purchases. Second-hand dealers bargained animatedly, many clenching matchsticks in their teeth, gesturing at clothing selected from the heaps in front of them. Several men, not part of the shopping process, had commandeered another section of the wall near us and were smoking and discussing the weekend's sport. The latest beat pulsated from portable radios. An ice cream vendor relaxed against his bike, waiting for customers.

The Bend-Over Bazaar was fun - an experience to be repeated.

THE WORST WEEKEND EVER

Matthew stood at the window looking out into the dark garden. He shivered with anxiety and cold as he listened to the high-pitched whine of the wind. The tree branches and bougainvillea creepers pounded against the windows and the roof of the house. This was no gentle, benign tapping and rustling of leaves and twigs such as one might expect in early March. This was not the strong breeze that jangled the wind chimes hanging from the eaves outside the lounge. In fact, he'd *never* experienced wind this strong in Zimbabwe. Perhaps in England when he was young (he tried to think back forty years or so), but never here. This was a primeval, ominous force that seemed to bend and twist and wrench everything in its path. He thought of the earthquakes, avalanches and hurricanes he and Margaret had seen on television in recent months. They didn't seem so remote tonight.

What made things worse was his realisation that there was no electricity. The face of their bedside clock was blank. The security lights that should be illuminating the perimeter of the house were not working. Nothing was working. The wind had taken control. Could it have blown down the power lines?

This was Friday night or the early hours of Saturday morning. What were their chances of having power restored if this, in fact, had happened? Would ZESA[20] do anything during a weekend? If damage were widespread, their emergency team wouldn't be able to cope anyway.

The wind continued to howl and wail. Matthew fumbled about on the floor on his side of the bed and found his torch. Margaret was fast asleep. She couldn't wear her hearing aid in bed, so from the time she turned off her bedside light, she entered a silent, lonely world. The torchlight wakened her now, and she sat up groggily.

---

20 ZESA: Zimbabwe Electricity Supply Authority

"What's wrong, Matthew?" she asked. Her husband was obviously wide-awake. He shone the torch towards his own face and enunciated his words clearly so that she could lip-read. "We've got another power cut. Can you hear the wind?" he asked. He knew this was unlikely, but the shrieking and howling outside was so ferocious, it was difficult to imagine that even a deaf person wouldn't be able to hear it.

"I can't hear a thing," said Margaret. "Come back to bed." She suddenly realised how cold it had become. "We're going to need the duvet."

Matthew pulled the cover over them both and climbed back into bed. Margaret snuggled up to him and fell asleep quite easily. Matthew tossed and turned. He couldn't stop thinking about their roof being damaged, their windows being broken or large trees smashing down onto the driveway.

He must have slept eventually.

A thin, grey light filtered weakly into the room. The alarm clock was blank, so obviously there was still no electricity. The sound of the wind was as intimidating as ever, possibly more so.

Book Club was at Mary's house that morning. Margaret didn't feel comfortable about leaving Matthew on his own – he was not his normal unfazed, energetic self – today he seemed very disturbed and looked worn out. Margaret never failed to appreciate his love and care and the trouble he took to reassure her when *she* had bad days. Especially that awful time years ago before her operation. She was fetching Shirley, however, as it was her turn to provide transport. Matthew had phoned Caroline and found that they, too, were without power. It was worse for them with three small children.

Although she couldn't hear the wind, she could see the effects: twigs and leaves littered the drive and their trees and shrubs gyrated alarmingly. Shivering uneasily, she went outside to her car and drove carefully through the debris to fetch Shirley.

Book Club dragged that morning. Conversations swirled about her in a cacophony of irritating and indistinguishable sound. She felt like putting her hands over her ears and escaping outside. She certainly was not in the right frame of mind to be pleasant, attentive or sociable. Luckily, Kumalo had electricity; otherwise Mary would have found hosting Book Club a nightmare.

She messaged Matthew, and he confirmed that there was still no power in Burnside. She would have to return to a gloomy, silent house and a depressed husband. Matthew wouldn't be able to watch rugby and she wouldn't be able to use the computer. She was worried about her freezer full of food. The fish would have to be cooked, she thought, if the power was not restored within the next twenty-four hours. It was another Catch 22 situation. People who had freezers kept them full, as incessant rumours of impending shortages made everyone nervous. If you had a full freezer, though, you ran the risk of losing millions of dollars worth of meat, fish and other basic foodstuffs if there were long power cuts.

The afternoon got colder and darker and she and Matthew felt even more desperate. How were they going to bath or shower? Matthew had phoned ZESA a number of times, and had been unable to get through.

"I suppose the whole of this side of town is trying to contact them to complain and to plead with them to do something," he said. "Caroline phoned to tell us that she'd take the children to bath at Irene's house. Jason will be coming over to borrow the camping stove. Theirs is out of gas."

That evening they grilled sausages over a wood fire outside in the braai patio. Although it was sheltered from the wind, it was anything but pleasant. Years ago, they'd enjoyed camping with the children. But you decided to rough it because you wanted to, not because you had to. They were too old for this sort of thing. Candles, romantic when dining out, weren't ideal for reading. They both felt frustrated and angry.

The next day the wind seemed even more frightening. Again they had awakened to a gloomy dawn. They boiled a large pot of water on the gas stove and both "showered" using a bucket. It was such a crude method of washing, when one was used to hot running water.

Margaret always felt depressed in winter on dull, cold, cloudy days. If they were living overseas it would be warm indoors and they'd be able to watch their favourite programmes on TV. They wouldn't have to worry constantly about trying to anticipate load-shedding and power cuts and trying to find gas.

Matthew agreed that this was the sort of thing they needed to consider. "I've been hearing rumours from Jason and Caroline about South Africa threatening to cut off power supplies to Zimbabwe, because we haven't been paying our bills. Perhaps 'quiet diplomacy' doesn't apply where large sums of cash are involved. You can't blame the South African government. Why should they keep pouring money into a bottomless pit?"

"If we had to leave Zimbabwe, I'd love to settle near Durban," said Margaret. "Anthony and Tracy are likely to start a family soon. It's hot and there's always an exciting buzz. We could combine the best of both worlds."

This was a tempting and feasible alternative, since they owned a flat at Umhlanga. Matthew worried about the racial situation in South Africa, though. Vicious crimes, frequently with whites as targets, were everyday events. It was also becoming obvious that certain government officials in South Africa were as corrupt as their "brothers" north of the Limpopo. President Thabo Mbeki was known in some circles in Zimbabwe as "Mandela's Revenge". South Africa could well go the same way as the rest of the African continent.

Speculation along these lines was horribly depressing.

The weekend dragged on with the wind not letting up for a single second. Monday came and went and there was still no power and still the wind blew. The residents of Hillside and Burnside were frantic. They were cold and tired and the painstakingly harvested food in their freezers had thawed.

On Tuesday afternoon the power came back on at last. The four long days had been among the worst Margaret had ever experienced. Their garden looked like a war zone. The drive had disappeared under alarmingly large branches and twigs that had been ripped and twisted off the trees. Thousands of leaves concealed the lawns. It would take ages to clear up the mess. Fortunately there was no damage to any of the buildings.

There'd been damage of another sort, though.

For the first time they were seriously reviewing their options. What would happen if they were to fall ill and need operations or procedures unaffordable in Zimbabwe? Everyone was nervous about deteriorating medical care and health facilities. And what would their lives be like if Caroline and Jason decided to emigrate?

Their lovely home was built for summer weather. The rooms were designed around rock features, which were part of the structure. When there was a power failure, the rocks seemed to absorb and retain the cold, and appeared almost alien.

When Caroline and Anthony were young children, life in Bulawayo had been wonderful. She and her friends often used to go window-shopping with the kids in the evenings. On Saturday or Sunday afternoons they'd take the children to the park for rides on the little trains, King Arthur and Queen Guinevere. The miniature railway was a service to the community run by Round Table. They'd buy tea and cream scones at the restaurant and, in between rides, watch the swans and ducks swimming about on the little lake around which the train ran. The park was beautifully kept in those days.

Early in December, the Mayor of Bulawayo would switch on the Christmas lights at a small ceremony in the park. The children's eyes would fill with wonder as Disney characters sprang up on the one side of the road, while, on the other side, fairy lights on the giant fir tree lit the nativity scene. Each Saturday evening during Advent there'd be carols by candlelight.

Small things. Simple things.

No one went to the movies anymore. Everyone stayed at home and watched TV or videos or DVDs. Most of the cinemas had shut down. The old department stores like Haddon and Sly and Sanders had closed. No one wandered around the shops at night any more. They'd almost certainly be mugged, and there was nothing to see anyway.

She and Matthew had taken their grandchildren to the park one Saturday recently; as they'd heard one of the trains was running again. It was more than twenty-five years since they'd been there. Weeds and litter had replaced the flower beds. Everything looked derelict.

Caroline arrived with the three little boys. It was just as well. Margaret was feeling melancholy and unsettled again.

The two older boys were very excited. They told her they'd seen a wriggly, brown snake in the garden. Little Ross leaped into her arms, and she hugged him tightly.

She'd always felt guilty about wishing her own children older. They'd gone to nursery school when they were very little, as Matthew had just started his own business and they'd had to rely on her teacher's salary until he got things going.

It was different with grandchildren, Margaret thought, bouncing Ross up and down on her knee. You wanted to savour every precious moment. You didn't want them to grow up. You wanted to hug and hold them and love them.

How could they leave?

April Book Club

What a relief! It was going to be a bright sunny day.

We had decided on a win/win. I would have Book Club outside in our newly covered patio if it was warm enough. Larry would then be able to watch Super 14 Rugby on TV in the lounge. The first match was an important one, as the two teams at the top of the log were playing each other. The Crusaders were taking on the Hurricanes – it would be an exciting contest. The Super 14 competition was well under way, and if you were a rugby fan, you hated missing any of the matches. I'd become converted about three years previously. I loved watching, and was confident that, apart from the mysterious realm of the scrum, I knew what was going on most of the time. I could yell "informed" abuse at the ref as well as Larry could.

"What's wrong with the ref, didn't he see that 'knock on'?" we would complain bitterly.

Or: "That ball wasn't thrown in straight. What's wrong with this guy? He's very quick to penalise the Sharks on *their* line-out throws!"

Or: "Ref, didn't you see that punch? Real handbag stuff, but that Ozzie lock threw a punch at Bakkies Botha. He probably deserved it, but...."

Etc., etc.

Although it was supposed to be relaxing, we were concerned that the South African sides were not as competitive as they should be. With black empowerment firmly in place, were the best *players* being selected, or were the best *black* players being selected? Along with Naas and Joel on "Boots and All", we speculated as to why it was that they were under-performing, and, specifically, why they were not scoring tries.

I had decided to try some new recipes. I'd made a 30-day muffin mixture and had tried out some choc-chip muffins earlier in the week. They were fine. Everyone loved samosas and I'd always wondered how to make them. They now cost $60,000 each to buy, so I'd decided to experiment. Our credit controller, Stephanie, in Harare had sent us her recipe and Patricia had tried it out laboriously (but successfully) the previous weekend. She'd had to phone Steph, though, to check how to fold them. It must have taken me at least two hours to put them together. How thick or thin to roll out the pastry was the first dilemma. The second problem was how big to cut the initial circle (which would then be divided into quarters). And what to use? A saucepan lid? A plate? A saucer? I eventually opted for a large side plate. Patricia had made me a "dummy" out of paper, which I had in front of me. I'd done the beef filling earlier in the week, so this, at least, was ready. Each samosa seemed to vary in size and shape. The worst ones were limp with the filling beginning to seep through the paper-thin pastry. I hoped that freezing them uncooked would be the solution.

I'd made Audra's lemon cheesecake for the first time. It was also time-consuming, but straightforward. I teamed this with my vanilla sponge cake, a wonderful recipe I'd been using for more than 30 years. The chiffon sponge always rose impressively and drew awed comments. The filling (whipped cream, chocolate flaky bar and strawberries) increased the height of the cake even further. I poured a hot choc-fudge icing over the top and decorated it with chocolate flakes and walnuts. My pizza was another old faithful that never failed. The dough always took ages to spread across the baking tray, though, and, of course, much longer if you were in a hurry.

While it was still dark, I got up to put everything together. I always seemed to have a last minute rush, no matter how hard I tried to avoid it. This time I was determined to enjoy having the meeting at my house, instead of worrying about it. I prayed that there would be no power cuts. If there were, I would be in trouble, as I had no back up. Our generator was at the factory and I didn't have a gas cooker.

Audra's presentation of food at her coffee shop, The Roasted Berry, was always superb, and I'd been inspired. A few weeks before, Margaret and I had gone there for lunch to celebrate Margaret's sixtieth birthday. We were enchanted by a lemon basket filled with herb fronds and tiny flowers that garnished her beef stroganoff. I'd borrowed Aud's book of garnishes and Patricia had photocopied various sections for the three of us. I knew there'd be no time for anything exotic, but at least I could use fruit, flowers and leaves effectively.

We were all looking forward to getting to know Yvonne, whom most of us had met for the first time at Mary's Book Club in March. Moira, her sponsor, was on holiday in South Africa, so Yvonne would be coming on her own.

It would be quite a small gathering, as Mary had to officiate at an inter-schools' athletics meeting, Stella was involved at a political think tank and Cheryl was out on a bee removal exercise. Petite Mary was to supervise the shot putt of all things! She'd been given a lesson on how to hold the tape and how to measure accurately. She preferred being a track place judge, she said. It was much easier.

Sunshine poured into the patio. My ferns blended harmoniously with colourful Busy Lizzies. The newly cut lawn looked well-tended and smelled clean and fresh. Dex, our boisterous Great Dane, was unusually quiet and well-behaved as he lay by the patio gate watching us. The early arrivals were chatting animatedly. I could tell that Margaret was managing better than usual. She was responding well to questions and conversing easily without having to ask for comments to be repeated. The acoustics must be quite good out there.

She was wearing a glamorous plum-coloured suit with purple lipstick to match. It was difficult to believe that she was a grandmother. She and Matthew would be leaving for the UK the next day. She reminded us that it was eighteen years since she'd last visited England, where she had been born and brought up, and so she was feeling both excited and apprehensive. What would it be like going back after all this time? Would everything be very different? Shirley and I wondered whether it had now also become a reconnaissance mission. Would it be possible for them to live there again if they decided to leave Zimbabwe?

I couldn't listen to all the book reviews, as I had to finish preparing the tea. Observations and remarks filtered through to the kitchen from time to time, though, interspersed with commentary on the Crusaders'/Hurricanes' game.

"Chris Jack always makes an impact...."

"I found her attitude to her parents very negative and depressing.... I prefer her biographies to her novels..."

"I agree... 'Precious Lives' and 'Hidden Lives' were brilliant...."

"By the way, has anyone got those two books? They're mine and I haven't seen them for ages..."

"The ref has awarded a penalty.... He's indicating that two of the Hurricanes' backs were offside.... "

Shirley was reviewing Nelson DeMille's 'Night Fall'.

"I love John Corey's smart-ass sense of humour. He has just had a fight with his wife, Kate. He says, 'I accept your apology.... I also think this was a liberating experience for us, a growing and affirming event ... in our relationship.' Thoroughly irritated by his flippant attitude, she responds, 'You're a total jerk.' 'What's your point?' he asks, presumably straight-faced."

I grinned. Like Shirley and Marilyn, I was a Nelson DeMille fan....

"... I believe that we can all make a difference in our little corner of the world.... That's why we're here..."

I listened carefully. Yvonne had made this comment. She wasn't just sitting there. She was voicing her opinions confidently. She was talking about her activities as chairlady of a steering committee for a school catering for special needs.

"At first they thought that I would take care of everything, because I was white. Then they realised that they, too, would be expected to contribute their time, skills and money. It was a learning curve for them and for me. I came to understand that I had to be clear about what I needed from them. That there was work to be done and that donations would not be pouring in from white-run charities..."

"Dan Carter somehow makes difficult kicks look ridiculously simple.... By the end of the season, he'll probably have more than 400 points to his credit - an amazing achievement... What a class act he is..."

"...Our own Bulawayo version of 'Desperate Housewives'..."
This was Marilyn. My ears pricked up, and I tuned in properly
again.

"We were sick and tired of our men going boozing together
every Friday afternoon after work." Marilyn was saying, amid
much laughter. "So some of us decided to get together on
Friday evenings. We have a great time. We have a few glasses
of wine and can sound off about our husbands and about men,
in general, if we feel like it. Or we can ignore the subject of men
altogether."

"Sometimes they'll phone and invite us to join them at
whatever club or restaurant they're at. It's weird! They can't
bear to think of us having a good time on our own!"

"Crouch and hold! Engage..." The referee was positioning
the two scrums. Only two minutes left...

It was time to serve tea. I'd put the plates of food on the table
in the dining room. I'd garnished the lemon cheesecake with
cream rosettes and drizzled lemon curd over it, as the recipe
had instructed. Beside the dish I had laid lemon leaves and
green and yellow lemon halves. It looked quite impressive. I'd
arranged small bunches of parsley among the warmed slices of
pizza and decorated the samosas with nasturtium flowers and
leaves. I hoped that my guests would focus on the nasturtiums
and not on the amateurish samosas.

Tea was a success overall, but the samosas were lousy. They
were leathery and chewy, rather than crisp and crunchy and the
filling was too bland. I should have used more curry powder.
Perhaps $60,000 each was not too much after all, if one took
into account the expertise required to make them.

Yvonne still had a little wine in her glass when the rest of the
group was ready to go. I persuaded her to linger over it. I was
looking forward to getting to know her, now that I no longer
had to worry about whether the tea was still hot or whether to
heat more milk for the coffee.

It was very easy to talk to our new member.

She told me that she believed we were going through this
terrible time because God had a purpose for us. She felt that

Zimbabweans (especially our young men and women) were unusually resourceful people, who could make a genuine difference wherever they went in the world.

"I have a son of 32 with Down syndrome," she told me. "He has taught me so much. He knows about God and speaks about Him. Jonathan is special."

I remembered reading an amazing book "Expecting Adam" about a Down syndrome child, born to highly intelligent young Harvard graduates. I asked Yvonne if she had read it.

"Yes," she said. "It's a wonderful story. I used to have a copy, but I lent to someone. I can't remember who."

I grimaced in sympathy. "It drives me berserk when I lend one of my most prized books out and never see it again."

"I believe that whoever has my book will pass it on, and that it will be read by those who will be comforted and enlightened by it," said Yvonne.

"Wow!" I thought. "A little different from my attitude."

"Do you know," she went on, "nothing has ever happened to me that I haven't been able to handle, including looking after a "Downie" and having to cope with the death of my first husband. You learn to get on with life. You learn to turn negatives into positives.

God is very real to me. He seems to have given me a built-in early warning system that makes me vigilant and alert when a crisis threatens. Some while ago, my second husband and I went to Messina. I'd been "warned" that something was going to happen. I had no idea what – I thought that we might possibly be involved in a car accident.

My husband wanted to visit his mother's grave. I stayed in the truck outside the deserted cemetery while he went in alone. He'd been very close to his mother. After a while, something made me look in the rear view mirror and I saw that a man was creeping towards me. He lunged through the open driver's window, demanding my handbag. I refused to give it to him. He drew a knife and threatened me with it. I clung stubbornly to my bag. It had R1,000 in it and my cell phone. It was mine, and I was not going to part with it.

Cursing angrily, he stabbed me several times in the leg, as we wrestled for possession of the bag. Finally, the strap broke and he pulled it through the window and took off. I had managed to press the hooter several times during the attack to alert my husband. He came rushing back and was horrified to find me covered in blood.

The South African police were fantastic. They took me to hospital to have my wounds stitched and made sure that I was given an anti-tetanus jab. They even gave us some money. The policeman, who'd been on duty when I was brought in, came up to the hospital and announced that his wife had insisted we spend the night with them.

'You Zimbabweans are something else,' he said, laughing. 'If one of us had been held up at knife point, he or she would have parted with the handbag, money, car or whatever was being demanded immediately. But not you guys! You insist on putting up a fight and endangering your lives!'

They were absolutely wonderful to us and treated us as though we were family. We were so blessed. This is the sort of thing I mean, when I say that I've always felt that God regards me and every one of us as special. You simply have to ask for what you need and then remember to say 'thank you' for what you have been given."

I was silent for a while. Yvonne glowed and I envied her certainty about God. I had to admit that I was not too charmed with Him at the moment. How could He allow the chaos in Zimbabwe? How could He permit the misery and the torment being inflicted on us by those in power? In my view, we'd all had quite enough of being tested, if that was what He was doing.

I was sure that she was going to be a very interesting addition to our Book Club. Controversial, too, perhaps. Neither Jeanette nor Margaret was enamoured of religion. I wasn't sure whether they were atheists, agnostics or simply sceptics. Margaret had loved Dan Brown's "The Da Vinci Code", for example. I suspected that part of her enjoyment of the book was Brown's disrespectful attitude to the Catholic Church. She was also genuinely fascinated by his concept of "the sacred feminine". She believed that women would do a better job of running things.

Not a bad idea, all things considered. Larry and Matthew might disagree, though. Shirley's husband, James, certainly would.

An Offer

Stella was lying, tilted at a fairly comfortable angle, gazing at the restful scene. A waterfall splashed into a clear, blue pool, spreading ripples that broke as gentle wavelets on the wet pebbles and stones at the water's edge. Luxuriant ferns undulated in the gentle breeze. Under different circumstances, she could easily have dozed off, lulled by the imagined sounds of the water and the bird calls in the glade.

Dr Sibanda was an impressive though diminutive figure in her spotless white uniform. Her huge brown eyes above her mask were filled with purpose and professionalism.

"Open wide, my dear," she said. "Let's take a look in there, shall we? Is this tender? Wider, please. Open a little more. Thank you." She probed at an old filling. "Hmm. There's a cavity here. There's not much enamel left, and the gum is receding. I'll have to repair this. Tandi, syringe, please."

Stella's stomach contracted and cringed involuntarily, as she anticipated the prick of the injection. She clenched her fingers and tensed, frowning at the poster attached to the ceiling above her. The glade was looking less tranquil.

Dr Sibanda stuck her gloved finger into Stella's mouth, gently pushing her lip down, so that she could ease the needle into her gum. She moved the instrument around. She seemed to be giving her more than one injection to numb the area. She chatted brightly about a dental congress she'd attended in Harare the previous week. Stella sat up to wash the blood out of her mouth, trying not to spit too vigorously, and wiped away the slimy trails of saliva quickly and surreptitiously. Her long hair was getting in the way of the rinsing process – she should have put it up before she left home that morning. Oh well, too late now.

"Try to relax, my dear," said Dr Sibanda. "You won't feel a thing. The injection will take effect immediately. Lovely rain we had yesterday."

"Yes, it was marvellous, wasn't it?" Stella mumbled distractedly.

After a moment or two, the dentist got down to business. "Can you feel this?" she asked. Stella shook her head and firmly shut her eyes.

Dr Sibanda screwed some sort of metallic clamp onto the side of her patient's mouth and then inserted the drill. Its screeching whine made even a one-sided conversation pointless.

In spite of the unpleasant activity focused on her mouth, Stella was miles away standing beside the waterfall, agitatedly considering the implications of an offer that had been made to her three days before.

She had received a rather enigmatic message on her cell phone, asking her to call a colleague regarding an interesting proposition that he would like to put to her on behalf of "someone else".

"Mr Tsvangirai would like to offer you the position of Deputy Secretary for Health," he told her when she spoke to him.

Stella was flabbergasted. "Why me?" she asked.

"Because you deserve it," he said cryptically. "But they need an answer right away."

"I can't make such an important decision immediately," said Stella. "I will have to think about this very carefully. But I am very honoured."

Stella found herself wondering whether she had imagined the conversation – it was so completely unexpected.

Granted, she was a nursing sister with many years' experience. Granted she had been a faithful servant of the MDC and particularly of her own constituency. And certainly, at one stage, she would willingly have laid down her life for Morgan Tsvangirai, if to do so would have benefited the people of Zimbabwe.

But now there were so many unanswered questions. The split in the MDC had caused her sleepless nights. All the hard work during the last six years, all the many hours that she and Terry had spent putting district structures in place for their ward was beginning to feel like time wasted. She often wished she could just stay at home and hide from the world. She was convinced that, somehow, she had let the people down. She had promised them a new beginning, she had offered them hope and she had talked to them of a brighter future.

Terry had told her not to be ridiculous. She must not blame herself for a situation that was beyond her control. They were mere cogs, he had insisted. Small fry in the party, and white. They couldn't be held accountable for the stuff-up their leaders had made of what had once been a viable and vibrant opposition.

So she lay back in the chair, imagining herself beside the waterfall, while Dr Sibanda and Tandi worked on her mouth. What should she do?

She was tempted to ask the girls at Book Club tomorrow what they thought. But she knew that there was little point. Most had returned to their former "head-in-the-sand" attitude, which left them feeling less despondent.

When she had told Terry, he had expressed strong reservations.

"But I might be able to make a difference," Stella had responded. "I might be able to help bring the two factions back together, somehow."

"Stels, you are so naïve," Terry had said impatiently. "Forget about politics. Concentrate on being a wife and mother. The children and I need you at home and there is so much that you can help me with at work. Our accounts aren't up to date and we need to submit our VAT return."

Stella was stubborn. She was determined to make up her own mind. Housework and book-keeping could wait. Twenty-four hours had not been enough time to decide and yesterday she had phoned Ms Khupe, the National Vice President, from whom the message had originated, and told her that she needed more time. This had been grudgingly allowed, but Stella knew that she had only one more day at the most, before they became impatient and retracted the offer.

The problem was that she was tempted to accept, and damn the consequences. The prospect of being a decision-maker was incredibly exciting. Intoxicating, in fact. Healthcare had always been her greatest love: it had been a vocation, not a career. This was an opportunity to use her training to help the suffering people in her beloved country.

Dr Sibanda finished filling the cavity with "cement" and smoothed the area carefully. "Bite," she instructed. "No. Harder. That's better. How does it feel?"

"UUUgh," Stella muttered, her eyes watering. Very difficult to answer a question with a huge numb tongue lolling about in her mouth and a clamp attached to her gum, threatening to turn her into a drooling idiot.

"Bite again," said the dentist patiently. "Now grind. Again. I'm going to put this into your mouth and I want you to bite down hard."

'This' was something solid that Stella imagined would show the imprint of the repaired tooth. She bit down energetically, then Dr Sibanda withdrew the 'tester', re-examined her handiwork and made a few minor corrections.

"Right, you can rinse now. You'll need to make an appointment for next month, so that I can check how the new filling is holding. You haven't got much tooth left in there."

While Stella was going through her rinsing and wiping routine, Dr Sibanda was doing *her* 'Do you floss regularly?' procedure. This always made Stella feel uncomfortable. Had bits of her last meal been trapped among her teeth?

She left Dr Sibanda's surgery with a numb mouth and a headache.

What should she do?

What should she do?

It was Monday morning and Stella was still vacillating.

She was alone at home and thinking about the concerns that had been voiced regarding violence in the MDC and Morgan's apparent failure to address the issue.

"Violence is a scourge," said a political colleague. "Zimbabwe has been afflicted with this terrible disease for over 150 years. The consequences of endemic violence have been compounded by our flourishing culture of impunity. Those who commit horrendous crimes are not punished. Instead they profit from what they've done.

You'll remember that attempt by some of the MDC youth to murder our Director for Security, Peter Guhu at Harvest House in September 2004. Don't forget that senior MDC officials were either involved or sympathetic to these youths. And don't forget that these same youths were not disciplined, but were actually re-employed and used to assault MDC staff members in May 2005.

We've fought against the evil that is ZANU PF. Our little team has fought a noble fight, I believe. We've made mistakes, but not with bad intent. We've been naïve and gullible, perhaps, but never politically cynical. I beg you not to be tempted by this amazing offer."

"This is like wrestling a crocodile," Stella thought, waves of exhaustion coursing through her.

There were many who cautioned her not to get involved in the high level cut-throat political arena.

"It's far too dangerous," they said. "You're crazy. Women have no place in politics. And certainly not white women in a black country."

There were business acquaintances who advised her to do something sensible like putting her energy and resolve into making money.

There were her activist friends who said that it was about time she had some recognition.

"This is your opportunity to do something for the sick and suffering," said her nursing friend Juliet. "Think how you could revolutionise the Health Service."

Many close friends had been worried. It was a wonderful accolade that was thoroughly deserved and a tribute to all her hard work. But they wondered whether there could be an ulterior motive.

Most persuasive of all considerations was the fact that her family was vehemently opposed to the idea.

Her pastor had been sympathetic. "You want to lead the people," he said. "But what if, by aligning yourself with this faction, you find yourself leading them wrongly? You, yourself have said that you cannot fight evil (if indeed they are evil) with evil. You must fight evil with good. It's the only way."

After several hours of contemplation, she realised that, without a sense of peace, she would be unable to function.

She telephoned Ms Khupe and thanked her very much for the confidence they'd shown in her. She said that, after lengthy consideration, she had decided that she would be unable to accept their offer. She wished them all the best for the future.

A few weeks later, she was offered the position of Secretary for Health on the National Executive of Arthur Mutambara's faction of the MDC.

Terry was supportive, as were most of her friends and colleagues.

Stella's statement was circulated by email to her friends and colleagues:

"I have accepted the position of Secretary for Health on the National Executive with Arthur Mutambara's MDC team. These last few months have been awful for so many of us... Good people have tried really hard to reconcile our beloved party and the rejection of their efforts has been devastating...

The MDC hand stands for truth, justice, non-violence, transparency and all-inclusiveness... These qualities will continue to be the driving force in everything I undertake...

...I will not be destructive or judgmental of Morgan's team and I promise that my goal and vision is unflinching... I pledge to give my all to remove the ZANU PF regime and to fight for freedom and democracy for all Zimbabweans..."

"Where are You Going, Little Boy?"

"Where are you going, little boy?" asked the woman kindly.

A small white boy wearing a bright red T-shirt, short trousers and trainers was trotting down the road towards her. Where was his mother?

"Pick me up and I'll show you!" he said, holding out his arms.

He was a lovely little child. She hoisted him up onto her back and he put his arms round her neck and his legs round her waist and clung on tightly. He was obviously used to being carried like this.

"Where are you going?" she asked again. "Where is your mother? It is dangerous to be walking on a road where there are motors. They go too fast and will knock you down."

"I am going to my house to get my chocolate," said the little boy. "My mother wouldn't let me take my chocolate to my granny's house."

"Where is your house, little boy?" asked his friend. Just then, a car came rushing past, and the lady said a quick thank you to UNKULUkulu[21] for the little boy who was safely on her back and not running across the road.

"Down there," he said, pointing to Avocet Lane.

When they got to a large house at the end of the lane, he started calling loudly, "Gogo! Gogo!" An elderly black lady came running out holding a cell phone.

"Gerald! Gerald! Where have you been? Everyone is looking for you. Your granny is crying and your mother is very cross. Why did you run away?" She scooped the child up and hugged him. Then she shook hands with Gerald's new friend and thanked her for her kindness.

The two women chatted for a few moments, while Gerald went to fetch his precious chocolate. His grandfather was already on his way to fetch him.

21 UNKULUkulu: God

"How wonderful African women are," said Margaret, smiling as she recounted the story.

Margaret and Matthew had been frantic when they realised that Gerald had disappeared shortly after Caroline had dropped the boys off with them for the morning. Baby Ross was fast asleep on Gertie's back, but Gerald had vanished. It transpired that he had climbed into his grandfather's truck, taken the remote control for the electric gate and quietly let himself out. He was determined to recover his chocolate.

"What was extraordinary," said Margaret, "was the fact that the lady who had looked after him had returned to her own employer's house and had told her "madam" the story of the little boy. Mrs Francis had then driven the two of them round to Avocet Lane to make sure that Gerald was safe and that his parents knew where he was. It seemed that, some years before, her own little son had run away and had ended up at the house right opposite Caroline's. How's that for coincidence, synchronicity or déjà vu?"

Margaret and Matthew had had a wonderful time in the UK and Europe. They had visited relatives they hadn't seen for years. Their hometown was brighter and cleaner than they remembered and the houses seemed more spacious. Their friends and relatives appeared to want for nothing: they had all the mod cons necessary to make housework relatively painless and most of them spent their annual holiday in Europe.

"My most thrilling experience was being at St Peter's Square in Rome and being blessed by the Pope," said Margaret. Smiling, she sat back to watch our reactions.

We stared at her.

"Are you serious?" I said.

This was our cynical Margaret, who had considered going on a "pilgrimage" to visit some of the locations mentioned by Dan Brown in "The Da Vinci Code".

"Totally serious and sincere," she said. "I knew you'd all be intrigued. It's impossible to describe the atmosphere in St Peter's Square, where all those thousands and thousands of people gather to be blessed by Pope Benedict. There was a kind of spiritual electricity, to which Catholics and non-Catholics alike responded. I found myself cheering wildly with everyone else when the Pope appeared on the balcony to address the crowd. Matthew was quite embarrassed."

Margaret always said that she believed in "goodness" rather than in any formal brand of worship. The "goodness" of the Pope had evidently caught her unawares.

We were standing round the tea table at Jeanette's house in town. This was "catch-up" time.

Earlier in the week, thieves had broken into our factory. They had come through the back entrance in the sanitary lane. Having cut a panel out of the external metal gate and gained access to the yard, they'd then gone on to remove wooden planks from the sturdy inner door. Apple Mac computers were evidently on their shopping list. Barry's beautiful new G5 had been taken, along with the CPU from one of the older Macs. They had also stolen all the software disks for the Mac programmes, our coffee maker, the vacuum cleaner, calculators and money from desk drawers. Fortunately, they hadn't stolen or vandalised any stock from the factory. It could have been a lot worse.

In the early hours of the morning, two alert members of the Paddonhurst neighbourhood watch had seen a taxi being pushed down a dark street in their suburb. They went to investigate. The vehicle had run out of petrol. (Only in Zimbabwe would the get-away car run out of fuel.) On the back seat were all sorts of interesting items: computers, disks, calculators and clothing. The neighbourhood watch personnel phoned the police, (who managed to find transport of their own for a change) and the thieves were taken to Central Police Station where, we were told, they'd had to use "minimum force" to extract a confession.

The thieves had taken a crowbar to the CPU and removed both the ram and the hard drive. Barry and Henry had shaken their heads in frustration, as all they had needed to do was to open a catch in the side of the unit. The CPU was wrecked. At first we had thought that, although it was filthy, Barry's G5 was intact. Unfortunately, it must have been dropped as well as dragged through the dirt, since we later found that the CD and

DVD drives had been damaged. We'd had to send it to Harare to be repaired once the insurance assessors had examined it.

I was devastated, I said, that our coffee maker had not been recovered. How was I to get my caffeine fix when I arrived at work? Instant coffee was not quite the same thing even though I did have a specially hoarded jar of Nescafé.

Moira had been uncharacteristically subdued earlier on during the book reviews. She now said rather shakily, "We were incredibly lucky last Saturday. Colin and I could have been killed.

We were on our way back after having spent the previous day in Francistown. The Plumtree border was horrific. There was one official only on duty handling both carbon tax and customs declarations. As you can imagine, the queue barely moved. A fight broke out as frustrated people started pushing and shoving one another. We watched the security guard blatantly take a bribe. He knew everyone was so desperate to be processed that no one was likely to want to make waves and slow things down by complaining about him. Eventually we got through, and by 9 am we were travelling along a straight stretch of road near Marula.

I had a magazine on my lap and was working on a Sudoku puzzle. Suddenly, I heard Colin gasp. I knew that something dreadful was about to happen and I didn't want to see what it was. So I kept my head down and prayed. The next moment something huge crashed through the windscreen on my side of the car, and suddenly I was swamped by whatever it was that had landed on top of me. Colin had slowed down, and had managed to retain control during the impact. He brought the car to a halt and rushed round to the passenger side.

I was screaming hysterically, 'Get it off me! Get it off me!' I had no idea what was crushing me. I only knew that I was desperate to be freed from whatever it was. I thought that the air bags might have been released suddenly for some reason. Poor Colin was in a terrible state.

A kudu[22] had come out of the bush. For a moment it had hesitated, and then it had attempted to leap to safety across the road, right in front of our car. It crashed into the front windscreen on the passenger side, shattering the glass. A severed limb and a spray of faeces had landed on me.

I was shivering uncontrollably, and was shocked and hysterical. I couldn't seem to open my eyes. They must have been glued shut with the animal's blood and muck. The smell was both terrifying and disgusting. I didn't think I'd been injured, but I felt bruised and sore, and I just wanted Colin to take me home so that I could get cleaned up.

He put me on the back seat and then drove on to Bulawayo as fast as he could. Luckily, the steering and the brakes were still sound, and he could see through his side of the windscreen.

We got to Malachite Park and Yvonne took over immediately. She and Colin got me into the shower and sluiced the muck off me. Then they ran a deep bath and immersed me in it. Yvonne washed my hair several times and I began to feel human again. Yvonne had thought that she was calm, but she brought me a cup of tea with three spoons of salt in it instead of sugar. When I was clean, our doctor arrived to examine me. I was fine, she said, and incredibly lucky. Friends of hers, who'd had a similar experience, had not been so fortunate. The wife had been killed and the husband paralysed.

If we lived in some town in New Zealand or Australia where we didn't know anyone, I wouldn't have had the wonderful support and concern of my friends. It's certainly a compelling reason for staying here."

She gave Yvonne a quick hug.

"There was no anti-tetanus serum available at either of the emergency chemists in town, but our pharmacist somehow managed to source the vaccine and I had the jab a couple of days later."

---

22 Kudus are a species of antelope – greater and lesser. Greater male kudus have long spiral horns and weigh around 220 pounds.

I looked more closely at Moira and noticed that she had several cuts on her face that she'd managed to conceal with make-up.

I remembered an occasion many years before, when we were driving home in a convoy from Plumtree School after a rugby match. Without warning, a buck had "flown" across the bonnet of the land cruiser directly in front of us. It had cleared the vehicle successfully and had disappeared into the bush. The entire convoy came to a halt to allow the driver of the land cruiser to recover.

When I went to thank Jeanette for having us, I found her rummaging in her kitchen cupboards. Finally, with a flourish, she produced a coffee maker.

"Use this one until you can replace your stolen one, Al," she said.

Moira was right. We were very fortunate to be able to rely on caring and supportive friends.

INFLUENCE OF THE EAST

2 June

Yesterday we got to the airport in plenty of time. A young South African couple was in the short queue in front of us. It's been ages since I've heard Afrikaans. They sounded like "Vaalies" from somewhere near Jo'burg, and I wondered where they'd been. They seemed happy, so they must have enjoyed themselves. Great. We need tourists so badly.

Then I realised that we'd been standing in the queue at the check-in desk for a while and nothing was happening. The desk attendant had vanished. There were more people behind us and a queue at the other check-in desk, which had also been abandoned by its official.

Had they overbooked again? We were annoyed with ourselves. Perhaps we should have tried to get there sooner. They always let the earlier arrivals on first. We wondered for a moment whether Mugabe and Grace could have hi-jacked the plane for another shopping trip. Not feasible, on mature reflection of course - he'd never take anything smaller than a Boeing.

A chunky Chinese man began having a furious exchange with a member of Air Zimbabwe's ground crew in the middle of the departure "hall".

We listened, hoping for a clue as to what was going on.

"Please do me a favour...." she was saying.

He was having none of her blandishments. "I come to Bulawayo yesterday and am to go back to Harare last night!" he shouted. "But there is no plane. I have to sleep in hotel here in Bulawayo. I come to airport this morning and you let other people on aircraft first. I have important meetings in Harare. I am not doing you any favour. You get me on the plane!"

A burly gentleman in the next queue decided to go for the jugular, too. "This is a disgrace. I've also been here since yesterday. You should give priority to people who were not able to get back to Harare last night. You brought us out on the airport bus. It was *your* transport. It was on time. Why aren't we on the flight? You people are bloody useless. Christ, I'm sick of your inefficiency!"

He was yelling at another official who'd suddenly materialised beside our check-in desk. This official seemed completely detached and gazed calmly at the wall above his head. Air Zimbabwe's ground personnel are not in the habit of issuing apologies.

When he had run out of steam, the official informed us that there was no ZESA. It hadn't occurred to us until now that it was actually quite dark in the hangar.

"So how does there being no power affect us?" I asked him. "Surely the plane can take off without it?"

"There are two planes on the runway," he said. (Unusual for Bulawayo – especially with both of them going to Harare.) "One has enough fuel to get to Harare. It is about to leave. The other has no fuel. Our generator has broken down and the manual fuel pump isn't working. There is nothing we can do until we can pump fuel into the plane."

So neither back-up system was working.

Larry offered them the loan of our generator. Charles could get it out to us within half an hour.

The official wasn't too sure about this. They were expecting someone from BP to come out to look at the pump.

There's seldom any sense of urgency in government-owned organisations.

I had complained to our travel agent, Rodwell Dlamini, when I was booking our tickets that the Chinese planes seemed to break down all the time. He found this amusing. "Better on the ground than in the air," he guffawed.

That had shut me up.

When I looked around again, I noticed that we were the only whites left in the departure hall. The black passengers were chatting to one another, or talking on their cell phones. One young man was considering driving to Harare rather than waiting to see whether a solution would be found. The burly man had disappeared. The Chinese chap was standing just outside the main door smoking a cigarette.

He came back inside for another round, but the airport staff had anticipated this, and had wisely retreated again. Larry and I were offered tea or coffee, much to our surprise. There was obviously a gas stove in the kitchen. We asked the Chinese gentleman to join us. He needed to calm down for everyone's sake.

He was a nice enough person, though understandably very frustrated. He'd been in Zim for nine years, and had set up an import business with relatives in Harare. He'd originally worked for the Chinese government assembling data from manufacturers. If the figures failed to show an improvement on the previous year's statistics, he'd been instructed to revise them. He also said that many Chinese were very poor and that large numbers died of starvation. *These* stats were never revealed.

At 11 o'clock we decided we might as well forget about going to Harare. As we got up to leave, the official we'd spoken to earlier came over to our table.

"We are thinking about your offer of the generator," he said.

The government's "Look East" Policy is extremely unpopular.

We've become accustomed to flying in jets like everyone else and don't enjoy having to step backwards in time to the turbo-prop era. But we can't afford to be paranoid. There's no other option unless you have the money to charter a private plane.

When Air Zim first hired the planes, everyone freaked.

Valerie swore the plane's tyres were completely smooth when she flew to Harare last month. She also was positive that she saw a couple of slits in them. She can be a drama queen, but she does work for Dunlop.

Tall guys always complain that they come close to decapitating themselves each time they fly in a Zhing Zhong[23]. You have

---

23 Zhing Zhong: a Zimbabwean slang word meaning cheap and of inferior quality - usually Chinese.

to remember to bend right over when you enter the plane. I keep forgetting. I'm 5'7" and I've bashed my head several times. When you walk through the cabin, you have to move in a straight line without taking your eyes off the open doors of the overhead lockers. They're really sharp, and if you're not careful, you'll find yourself bloody and battered. The planes are not designed for westerners with lanky legs and long torsos.

Sean read somewhere that Zhing Zhongs were built for island hopping, and were never intended to travel distances that lasted longer than twenty minutes. Marilyn was relieved to discover that their engines are made in America or Canada. The most important part of the plane was likely to be reliable, she said.

We're not allowed to refer to the planes as "Zhing Zhongs". And the tiny cramped Chinese buses they use in Harare aren't "Zhing Zhongs" either. We're told they have paper-thin bodywork that you can put your fist through. These Asian sardine cans are very uncomfortable, especially if there's standing room only. Passengers have to bend their heads so they don't connect with the roof. And since the roads are full of potholes, there must be plenty of bruises.

We're all aware that China wants Africa's raw materials to power its ever-expanding economy. Recently I read in an article that, in 2005, trade between Africa and China reached the $40 billion mark – having doubled every year for the past decade. Thirty percent of China's oil now comes from Africa. Although Beijing insists that it isn't their policy to meddle in a country's internal politics, it doesn't mean that business deals have no influence on politics. It means that China imposes no Western-style provisos on improving human rights or cleaning up corruption as a condition for aid and trade. It also means that our government won't lose essential "financial props" if the West stops investing or slaps further sanctions on them.

The unwelcome presence of China in our lives is becoming more and more evident.

The Glorious Summer of Politics

"He's frightening!" Moira had said, sounding worried. "He's arrogant, and behaved really badly when he was being interviewed by a South African journalist. Everyone says he looks the quintessential black dictator. Staring eyes. Rabid. And the rhetoric he spouts is as bad as Mugabe's."

We were delighted, at last, to have the video of his controversial SABC Africa interview to watch so that we could decide for ourselves. Larry and I (and various other members of Bulawayo's business community) were to attend a meeting at which he would be speaking the following evening.

Arthur Mutambara was certainly not relaxed during the "Hard Talk"- type interview. He was irritated by the discourteous manner of questioning and the constant interruptions. Instead of having a genuine desire to ask polite but probing questions, the interviewer appeared smugly antagonistic and favoured an interrogation approach. Obviously a fan of the BBC's Tim Sebastian.

When he was allowed to develop an idea, Professor Mutambara came across as highly intelligent. He was angered by such questions as: "Are you your own man?" The interviewer must have been influenced by an article in "The Herald" that (according to a political analyst) attempted "a character demolition and demonisation job". Mutambara reacted passionately to this allegation, saying that *he* was a realist. He accused his interviewer of being "an apologist".

Stella was watching the interview with us, and we all had the same impression. Prof. Mutambara was obviously hot-headed. He needed practice and grooming, so that he wouldn't be so easily needled. He appeared sincere and determined to take an active and constructive role in opposition politics. Larry was very irritated by the ill-mannered antics of the journalist, and said that he would have walked out had he been the professor. We all deplored the way questioners on this type of programme appeared to want to score points the whole time, trap the angry interviewee into making rash statements and dominate the proceedings themselves, rather than elicit information. Professor Mutambara was a tall, strong-looking man with a very large shaven head housing the formidable intellect for which he was well known. His career summary read as follows: "A former Standard Bank Director with responsibilities in seventeen different African countries. A Research Scientist and Professor of Robotics and Mechatronics from the Massachusetts Institute of Technology (MIT) and NASA, with business experience and skills as a Management Consultant with McKinsey and Company. High technology expert and leader, global strategy specialist, and an entrepreneur who advises senior managers and business leaders of global companies. Community leader, public intellectual and activist extensively involved in socio-economic issues in both the US and Africa. An author of three engineering books and 27 refereed papers. A Rhodes Scholar, with an MSc (Computer Engineering) and a PhD (Robotics and Mechatronics) from Oxford University, UK and a BSc (Hon) (Electrical Engineering) from UZ. He is currently the managing director and CEO of Africa Technology and Business Institute in Sandton, South Africa."

In other words: someone you would really like to have on your team if you had to try to pick up the pieces of a once-successful country. Someone who could confront Mugabe (a man of no mean intellect himself) and play the game of political chess with him. (Perhaps that was why he'd been nicknamed King Arthur.)

These days, everyone pointed fingers at everyone else. Had most or all prominent figures in the increasingly dirty world of Zimbabwean politics been bought by Mugabe and ZANU PF? Had the CIO infiltrated the various levels and structures of opposition parties and factions? And not only the opposition parties, but church hierarchies as well? Was there any public figure one could trust? Look what had happened to Jonathan Moyo, originally one of Mugabe's sternest critics. Suddenly he metamorphosed into the sycophantic spin-doctor, who effectively shut down all access to the media for anyone in opposition, from the MDC to the various NGOs.

Arthur Mutambara had been one of the pioneers of radical resistance politics at the University of Zimbabwe in Harare. In 1988, as Secretary General of the Students' Representative Council, he and his fellow students organised the first post-independence student demonstration against ZANU PF. They astutely separated the president from his government, arguing that they were supporting his campaign against corruption. The police violently suppressed the student uprising. A year later the police blockaded the campus and tear-gassed the student residences, as a reaction to their celebration of the previous year's demonstration. Arthur Mutambara, who had been elected president of the SRC, condemned this as "state terrorism at its worst". He was arrested and detained and, after further student unrest, the University was closed for the first time since independence. (Since then, it has been shut down many times, often the consequence of strikes and demonstrations.)

He had stood toe to toe with Mugabe as a young man in the rosy era of the eighties, insisting, even then, that there was something rotten... Morgan Tsvangirai, who was secretary-general of the Zimbabwe Congress of Trade Unions, had issued a statement supporting the students and condemning the government's over-reaction.

At a clandestine meeting, Professor Arthur Mutambara spoke to us, without notes, of his vision for the country. He said that ZANU PF had to be defeated and the all-pervasive ZANU culture eradicated. This was the sort of culture, he said, that made children and their parents believe that it was the norm to leave school to deal in foreign currency and fuel. The economic situation was unsustainable. The ruling party was the enemy, not the "other faction" of the MDC. He referred to Morgan Tsvangirai as his "brother" and his "hero". He said that Zimbabwe needed South Africa, SADC and the rest of the world to assist in the battle to remove "the dictator". He reiterated what he had said in his acceptance speech, that all the democratic forces in Zimbabwe needed to "engage" each other. Unity of purpose was essential. We needed to work together to reclaim our country. Title to land was necessary if there was to be investment in Zimbabwe. He said that our "generational mandate" was the economy and economic empowerment. He insisted that this generation "demanded the fruits of independence".

He endeared himself to me when he spoke of President Mugabe's ruinous 'Look East' policy. He said that the Chinese had a habit of off-loading their rubbish onto Third World countries such as ours. The Zimbabwean people did not appreciate the Zhing Zhong planes and buses, and resented being sold shoes that fell to pieces in two months. "We must not accept their CRAP!" he thundered. "They are perfectly capable of producing quality goods, which they sell to First World countries. This policy is a clear indication of their attitude to their esteemed Zimbabwean partners."

He spoke rapidly and articulately and we listened carefully and critically to every word. We were there to judge him as an alternative to Morgan Tsvangirai; as a black politician who might be corrupted by the twin temptations of wealth and power (as had so many others past and present) and as a person who could offer us hope.

There were many questions and concerns. One of the businessmen present said that a solution had to be found NOW. His business could not survive beyond the end of the year in the prevailing economic climate. We could not wait until 2008 or 2010. The whole country was about to collapse. What was his plan for the present? Mutambara replied that it would be both impossible and irresponsible to promise anything in the short term. Strategies had to be developed and put in place.

Another businessman had not been convinced that the Professor's entry into politics was either wise or helpful in terms of confronting the real problem: namely Mugabe and the ruling party. He deplored the split in the MDC. He, too, had been very unhappy with the interview on SABC Africa.

"I am most concerned about certain remarks you made in your acceptance speech, Professor Mutambara," he said. "I take issue with your comments about the liberation struggle, and the liberation war legacy. I worry about your warning to Western governments to refrain from aggression against us. You say that you are 'anti-imperialist' and 'anti-colonialist'. I am unimpressed by your reference to embracing 'Pan-African ideals'. Where has reliance upon the region got us? Which African leader in the region has spoken against Robert Mugabe's human rights abuses? Who has taken him to task for his treatment of his own people? Instead they honour him by naming a road after him in Malawi. It seems to me that you are anti-white and that you believe that our role here is very limited."

Prof. Mutambara appeared rather annoyed by such comments and questions.

"You must understand," he said, "that we have to work within the context of African politics – Realpolitik. I am an African leader, seeking to establish my credibility with other African leaders and their governments. I cannot appear to be a puppet of the West. This party would effectively be dead and buried, if I were viewed as such. We have to operate from the springboard of the liberation struggle, since all Africans from grassroots level to those in positions of power identify with the aspirations of that conflict."

His questioner remained unconvinced and left the meeting shortly afterwards.

One of the women present said that Zimbabweans had to act themselves. It was counter-productive to rely on President Mbeki who had done absolutely nothing to help the suffering people. Professor Mutambara responded that, while it was indeed necessary that we help ourselves, it was Vorster[24] who had brought the Rhodesian Front government to its knees. In the blink of an eye, Mbeki could do the same to ZANU PF. The reality of the situation was that Mbeki was viewed as Africa's

24 Balthazar Johannes (John) Vorster: Prime Minister of South Africa from 1966 to 1978.

leader. His power and influence were huge, just as Vorster's had been. His intervention had to be sought.

Stella drew Prof. Mutambara's attention to the fact that he had not been in the country in 2002. "With respect, Professor Mutambara," she said, "you were not here when the light in the eyes of all Zimbabweans went out. It was our most terrible hour. Mr Mbeki said that the election was free and fair. It was anything but free and fair. People died then, and have died since."

She spoke also of the present. She pleaded for action on behalf of the many impoverished, starving people (particularly in the rural areas) whose hope in the future had been destroyed. The professor listened to her emotional appeal with empathy and concern. He and his team (which included Stella) would be visiting rural communities the following day. I knew that she would be bringing the people her own unique brand of compassion and love, as she toured hospitals without drugs and schools without teachers.

Many spoke of the need for unity. They urged Professor Mutambara, Vice-President Gibson Sibanda and the Hon. Dave Coltart to try to find ways of burying their differences with the "other MDC". After months of agonising, Dave had decided to join Mutambara's MDC to work "in conjunction with colleagues who share a similar vision for a new Zimbabwe and who are committed to using the same means I am to reach that goal". He promised to continue his efforts to unite the two factions. "I remain absolutely convinced that the struggle for democracy will be severely handicapped so long as we are divided," he said.

It certainly was an interesting evening.

The following day Larry and I had been invited to attend a luncheon meeting with Morgan Tsvangirai. We planned to ask questions about the way forward, something that neither faction of the MDC seemed clear about in the short term. There had been a number of contradictions, it seemed, in Tsvangirai's declared strategy. Was there going to be mass action? His faction had said both "yes" and "no". We'd also been hearing about President Tsvangarai's threatened "winter of discontent". Would this "be made glorious summer"[25] by doing absolutely nothing effective yet again, we wondered.

The MDC leader hadn't changed since the last time we saw him at a rally in Centenary Park before the fiasco of 12 October. He has a big, round, jolly face and an engaging, relaxed manner. He always dresses informally in an open-necked shirt and casual trousers. Very different from the Professor's impeccably tailored dark suit of the previous evening. Morgan Tsvangirai appears to be a homespun man of the people, while Arthur Mutambara is very much the cultured, sophisticated academic.

He talked about the state of the nation and the fact that the Zimbabwean economy was unlikely to survive much beyond three or four months. He referred to the regrettable split in the MDC as being a fait accompli, and commented that the two factions needed to co-exist and focus on their common target: Robert Mugabe and ZANU PF. The MDC's new "Road Map" envisaged bringing Mugabe to the negotiating table through pressure both from inside and outside the country. A new constitution would be drafted and then free and fair elections would be held. Kofi Annan and President Mbeki would provide the external pressure. Mugabe's succession paranoia was having a negative effect within his own party.

The national mood favoured action, he said in response to questions from his lunch guests. Fear was very much a reality, so a programme was needed that was sustainable. A strategy to build the momentum was necessary. What was required was not just change, but a serious transformation. The people's expectations had to be fulfilled. He foresaw a transitional government running the country, as had been the case in South Africa.

President Mbeki had nothing positive to show so far for his presidency, President Tsvangirai maintained. His "quiet diplomacy", tantamount to a protection of Mugabe, had failed. The World Cup of 2010, scheduled to be held in South Africa,

---

25 From *Richard III*: *"Now is the winter of our discontent/Made glorious summer by this sun of York..."*

might be an important motivating factor. If there were no confidence in South Africa, then problems would arise, doubts would be voiced and internal and external pressures would be brought to bear that could threaten Mbeki's legacy.

I listened and made notes. What was fascinating was the similarity between what Professor Mutambara had said at the previous night's meeting and what President Tsvangirai was talking about now. They both wanted the electorate to focus on the common enemy. Each faction thought that the other had been infiltrated. Both expressed a desire for unity and admitted that the split had seriously weakened the MDC. Each insisted categorically that many approaches to the other faction had been made, but that these had been rejected. It was evident that they needed to talk to one another through a mediator acceptable to both parties.

"President Tsvangirai," I said, "it is absolutely imperative that the MDC operates as a unified force. You cannot allow this situation to continue. The two factions must come together and unite so that you can oppose ZANU PF effectively."

I was the only woman there. President Tsvangirai stopped fiddling with his cap and gave me his full attention. He had been twirling it about in his hands, and it looked as though he was preparing to leave. I wanted to have my say before he did so.

"I have tried to talk to them many times," he said. "But I have made absolutely no headway. They keep accusing me of violence. What more can I do?"

"No, President Tsvangirai," said Larry. "That is not so. The worst that has been said of you is that you have not punished the people responsible for violent acts. At Professor Mutambara's meeting last night, everyone spoke of you with respect. Mutambara himself said that you were a Zimbabwean hero."

President Tsvangirai had looked very hurt when he spoke of the defection of men with whom he had been close. Gibson Sibanda was one such person. They had worked together for twelve years, he said. Yet, at the previous night's meeting, Vice-president Gibson Sibanda had said that he had tried to reason with his friend unsuccessfully on a number of occasions. Clearly, there were all manner of misconceptions and misrepresentations. Was Morgan Tsvangirai being misled?

On 24 February 2006 Eldred Masunungure, chairman of the political and administrative studies department at the University of Zimbabwe, wrote:

"The combination of Mutambara and Tsvangirai would be an even bigger threat than the united old MDC. The two leaders have different but strong and complementary support bases. In that combination, opposition politics (could be) rejuvenated and re-energised. This would completely change the political landscape of the country."

But Zimbabwe was in meltdown. Would anyone act decisively before it was too late?

Rivers of People

It was only a week after payday, and the workers were already jockeying to borrow money to take them through the long month of July. Prices had shot up again, everything from milk to sugar, from fuel to cooking oil. The only thing that had not rocketed upwards was bread, and this was, no doubt, because 282 bakers had been arrested the previous week for selling their product above the controlled price. Bakers (like all other manufacturers) had to put their prices up to accommodate such increases as a 280% hike in three months in the cost of electricity and a 60% increase in the cost of flour. What was the point of operating at a loss? They might as well shut down.

Our factory manager's mood was bleak. He was a talented, sensible young man with superb organisational abilities and an excellent grasp of politics and economics. Everyone in the company respected him, including the older men who worked under him. He had a gravitas well beyond his years, and frequently found himself giving advice to those old enough to be his father.

"If I had a valid passport, I would leave this place tomorrow," he said sadly. "I would take my family away from here and never come back. Or I would return only if the situation improved. Life is really dreadful at the moment. The tougher it gets, the more dependants you find yourself having to look after. People out of work seem to be getting lazier and lazier. They're quite happy to sponge off those relatives who are working. My father-in-law visited us last weekend and made it clear to my wife that we should look after him. This is a man in his early fifties, who, although he is unemployed, is perfectly capable of working.

I have my sister's two sons living with me at the moment. You'll remember that she died of AIDS last year. The younger boy is HIV positive. He needs constant care, as he is very ill. The older boy of twenty was fired from a temporary job recently, because he was afraid to be on his own one night when his partner was ill. It wasn't a dangerous area. He was working as a security guard, and they operated in pairs. Without notifying his employers, he just left his beat and came home. I was furious, not only because he had lost his job, but also because he didn't even seem concerned. I had found the position for him so that he could make a contribution to our living expenses. I've told him that he can stay with us – we won't throw him out on the street - but we won't be feeding him anymore. It sounds hard, but I've had enough of seeing my two children being deprived of such things as oranges because my useless relatives are not prepared to make an effort to help themselves."

He took a deep breath and shook his whole body vigorously, as if trying to shrug off the rage and despair that consumed him. "When you paid us our bonuses in 2004, I was able to buy a sound system, a kitchen cupboard and chairs in the course of two months. Now I can't even budget. And I can't send groceries home to my parents in Tsholotsho as I used to do. I've pleaded with them to look after their grandsons, but they've refused. You whites are so lucky that you don't have this extended family millstone to contend with. Honestly, it's killing me, and our lack of privacy as a family unit really upsets my wife."

Poor man. I felt so sorry for him. He and Iris worked hard to support their family. Because of their extended family "culture" that allowed parasitic, often distant relatives to leech off those who had jobs, he could give his children very little. The "system" obviously caused great resentment and heartache for ambitious young parents.

"What do you think about the MDC now?" I asked. We were sitting in his office chatting, having reviewed the work tickets for the following week. It was some time since we'd discussed politics. I really enjoyed our discussions; as they gave me an insight into how intelligent young black Zimbabweans thought and felt. He had been an ardent MDC supporter for six years, and, having attended many rallies, was qualified to give an informed opinion.

"I'm sorry to say that I've lost hope in the MDC," he said. "I've lost hope that they will ever get our country back for us, since I don't think they are strong enough now to overcome ZANU PF. I attended a rally just before the senate elections last year, and I was no longer convinced by Tsvangirai's leadership qualities. He is undoubtedly a courageous man, but I don't think he's the right guy for the position. As for Mutambara, the people in the rural areas don't know much about him. Someone in Tsholotsho asked me the other day whether he was a soccer player. With the World Cup in South Africa to look forward to in 2010, people are even more soccer-mad than usual."

"Would you say that the constant focus on football is a ruse to deflect people's attention from critical issues?" I asked.

After awful weekends of politically inspired violence, when people had been tortured by ruling party thugs, bill-boards and newspaper headlines would inform the public that CAPS United had unexpectedly beaten Highlanders or that a popular player had been dropped.

He gave this question some consideration and then answered it rather enigmatically.

"You should come to Barbourfields sometime to watch a soccer match when Highlanders are playing," he said. "If Highlanders' supporters moved from the stadium into the streets, our protests could really be effective. You should see the people on the terraces. There are thousands and thousands of them. They all sing uncomplimentary songs about the president and the government. They make every effort to embarrass visiting ministers who are guests of honour. They feel brave, in spite of the riot police, because they know that the cops can't single out the culprits. So the police have to pretend not to hear the loud comments and the songs. It is both satisfying and amusing. But after the match, everyone goes home and nothing changes.

People in Matabeleland are terrified to protest too loudly. No one has forgotten Gukurahundi. We can never allow this to happen again. We know that HE would do anything to make a point. I can't answer for the Shonas in Mashonaland. Surely they are responsible for what HE is? The Shonas here basically think like the Matabele. They are sick and tired of what is happening.

The two of you should take a drive out on Steelworks Road one evening after work. You would be amazed to see the thousands of people flowing like a river, some walking and some cycling to get home. Most are shivering with cold, as they cannot afford warm clothes any more. Few can afford to pay $100,000 for emergency taxi[26] fares.

As you know, there's an alternative method of travel: the commuter train, which leaves Luveve Station at 5 am. Tickets cost only $20,000, but in order to catch the train, you need to be up by 3.30 am to be at the station by 4.30 am. Every day there's a stampede for a limited number of places, with people pushing and shoving one another, desperate for a tiny space on a train, which has old, dirty carriages with no lights. In the evening, there are two trains: one at 4.45 pm and the other at 6.45 pm. If you finish work at 5 pm (as most people do), you would have to catch the later train, and you would probably get home at about 8.30 pm. Then up at 3.30 again… It's terrible that we have to live like this especially in winter when it's freezing cold."

He looked at me sadly and shuddered again.

"It's becoming increasingly difficult for parents to send their children to school. In January this year the fee for a primary school child was $150,000 per term. In May the tuition fee per child was increased to $2,500,000. The fee for a secondary school child in the first term was $800,000. In May it was increased to $4,000,000. This is a crippling situation for the average parent. How does he educate his children?

I feel desperate sometimes, too, when I see how people's values have changed. These days, people only respect someone if he gives them money. It doesn't matter if it comes from a

---

26 Emergency taxis (ETs) are privately-owned vehicles into which as many people as possible are packed. Safety is not a consideration.

thug. As long as it's money, that's the only consideration. What have we become?"

We whites were trying with limited success to live normal lives. We were outraged by the corruption, the inefficiency, the continuous power cuts and inflation.

But most of the black people were struggling merely to survive.

INTERESTING TIMES

11 July

Dennis catapulted through our front door, as he usually does, in an untidy flurry of arms and legs.

"I'll be getting petrol next week!" he crowed.

"I've heard that one before," Larry snorted. "You said that last week and the week before. What's different?"

"No chance of things going wrong," said Dennis, "I've paid for it and I know it's on its way. This time it's for sure."

Larry shook his head and went back to his office. He wasn't convinced.

Dennis was fizzing with energy. We offered him a cup of coffee and he sat down for a few moments to recount his latest escapade. He finds his precarious lifestyle as the owner of a service station truly exhilarating.

"I spent over an hour at the cop shop yesterday," he said, drawing his chair closer. "And do you know why? Some guy, who brought in a car to be repaired, is accusing me of stealing two light globes and a radiator cap. The stupid bastard owes ME $9,000,000. So the cops arrest ME and haul ME off to answer their questions in one of those small offices where they interrogate people. And they wanted to take my fingerprints. You know me. I don't keep quiet. So I really gave them the gears and told them that the person responsible for all the recent thefts in our workshop has gapped it to Zambia. Nothing to do with me at all. That slowed them down a bit. Anyway, I've got to go back there tomorrow. They mustn't think they can give me a hard time..."

Dennis loves his hair. He runs his fingers through it all the time while he's talking. Then he pulls the cluster of long ginger ringlets into the nape of his neck and teases them tenderly into a ponytail. He's the epitome of a Rhodesian hippie from the sixties. He usually wears a leather jacket, shorts (in the middle of winter), long stockings and suede boots. In the sixties he'd have had a comb in his sock.

"Dennis," I said to him, "this whole fuel thing really confuses me. I never know these days what's legal and what's not. What about this consignment you're bringing in? Legal or black-market?"

"Strictly legal," said Dennis with a grin. "You know me! But, jokes aside, it IS legit. And it IS coming through early next week."

I asked him to explain how it all worked.

Dennis loves to instruct.

"Well..." he began, putting down his cup and settling himself more comfortably.

It was obviously going to be a long, convoluted account.

"...There are three ways of purchasing fuel legitimately at the moment. If you want to import, say, thirty thousand litres of fuel you have to start by getting a proforma invoice from an oil company. You have to use a Foreign Currency account in order to pay for it. You take your proforma invoice to your bank and the bank transfers the money from your FC account to an overseas account. The account holder overseas (information not to be divulged!) pays the oil company here in Zim, and then the oil company guarantees that it will supply your fuel within ten days."

"Or..." he paused to check whether we were paying attention.

We were.

"Or ...you can purchase fuel through a third party. Any Tom, Dick or Harry can bring fuel in, but it must be taken to an oil company to be pumped into their tanks and checked for contamination. The dealer will have sold it to me in advance at a certain price. The next step is to pay a handling fee of so much per litre to the oil company who will then deliver it to me in one of their tankers. I will sell it on to the public at the current US$ rate. This can change as often as three times during the course of one day."

Patricia was amazed. "You mean you could change the selling price at the pumps while vehicles are actually queuing up?" she asked. "How would you do that?"

"Easy," Dennis laughed. "You simply adjust the meter whenever you have to."

"But surely your customers get angry if you do that in front of them?" I asked him.

Dennis looked at me rather pityingly. "Not at all," he said. "They want the fuel. They just have to like it or lump it. I haven't had a riot on my hands lately."

"There again," I reminded him, "you haven't had fuel for ages either, have you?"

"True," said Dennis, completely unfazed. "Now the third way of getting fuel is through the Oil Companies when they get it through our government-owned fuel body, NOCZIM."

"So when did you last get fuel through them?" we queried.

"I've only had it once in six months," he told us. "When NOCZIM get it, they make sure that the party faithful who own service stations and various affirmative action types are the lucky recipients. Guys like us whiteys come last."

We shook our heads in disbelief. "How do you cope?" we asked him.

"I just make a plan," he said airily. "I thrive on the adrenaline rush I get from manoeuvring and ducking and diving. But when all three of those routes fail, you just have to rely on your black-market suppliers."

He took off through the door.

Two seconds later he was back.

"I'll pop in tomorrow and have tea with you and tell you how to double your money in a month, if you bring in nine loads of fuel. If you have money available, you can keep rolling it over. It takes the bank ninety days to do this. So which way is better?"

With a grin and a wave, our friendly entrepreneur took off again.

It took Patricia and me a while to get our feet firmly back on the ground. We were checking calendars to make sure that the apostrophe in "Heroes' Day" had been positioned after the s and not before it.

15 July

We were very busy yesterday.

The extractor fans in the factory were humming and whirring. The printers in the offices were sawing and droning. The phones were ringing continuously. Henry was working flat out trying to calibrate the colour on the new Apple Mac that had just arrived from South Africa. We'd finally managed to replace the stolen computer. The other two artists haven't been able to do much for the last few weeks as only one of the operational computers holds existing job files. It was nearly teatime and the kettle was almost boiling. Patricia was working on a stock schedule and Nikki had almost completed her bank reconciliation. Larry was doing new price lists and Marilyn was on the phone to a customer. I was doing my final check on the A4 Page-a-Day diary.

Next minute... Without warning... everything came to an abrupt stop. Some omnipotent finger had flipped a switch again. Or some ageing part of a vital machine had finally died.

Our offices and the studio were plunged into darkness. The extractor fans stopped. Every computer in the building went blank. Howls of rage and frustration could be heard.

"Oh, shit! Oh, no, that's the second time my calibration has been ruined!" This from Henry.

"Oh, my God. I think I forgot to save that last part. And I was so close to balancing!" wailed Nikki.

"Oh, fuck!" This from Marilyn. "I had such trouble getting through to Hippo Valley. And now I've lost him again."

Marilyn uses the F-word with great enjoyment and gusto when she's mad or when she's trying to shock people. But on this occasion she was livid, and it came from the heart.

"Oh, fuck!" she said again. "I left home this morning with wet hair after having had a cold bath. You'll be amazed to hear that we had a power cut. Surprise, surprise. I come here and Robbie is just about to make me a cup of coffee, and what happens? I might as well go shopping. I can't do any work."

"Not much point in going shopping," said Michelle, lighting a cigarette. She'd just emerged from her black hole of an office. "I've checked outside and the power is out next door and across the road, and the traffic lights are dead."

I asked Marilyn how last week's 'Desperate Housewives' had gone.

Marilyn said that Fiona had had a great time.

"After a couple of glasses of wine, she was in full swing. She said that, although she loves New Zealand, she really misses the shared history she has with so many of us here. It's something that can't be replaced, she says, even though you make friends where you've settled. Their kids do so much that they're bound to meet lots of people at school functions."

"Actually," she went on, "we've re-christened our group 'Desperate Midwives'. As the girls began to arrive, our Staffie's waters broke. Margie took charge at once. She called for towels and was just in time to deliver the first puppy. It came out in a transparent sac, which she peeled off. Then, to get its circulation going, she rubbed the new baby with a towel. Steffie started licking it immediately and bit through the umbilical cord, which she ate. Within moments, the next puppy arrived, and this went on until there were seven: two males and five females. Steffie cleaned every one of them. She didn't leave any mess for me to sort out."

Nikki asked whether the women spent the evening bitching about their husbands.

Marilyn said that they did sometimes if they felt really pissed off. Elaine's husband, for example, thought it was quite OK to play squash three evenings a week. Then on Friday afternoons he'd have lunch with "the boys". Their Friday lunches went on all afternoon. After "lunch" they'd go off together to OMs, Queens or BAC for a few more drinks.

"One or two of the husbands are control freaks, and want to know where their wives are every second of the day. Margie's husband messages her three or four times every hour to check where she is," Marilyn went on. "Honestly, he's unreal. So our get-togethers are a sort of safety valve. The girls are there to relax and have a good time with other women who are left high and dry every Friday night. It's not as if we're out trawling the pubs. We're at one another's houses.

The men are always asking questions about what we've been doing and what we've been discussing. They were perfectly happy to leave us on our own on Friday nights before. Now, many of them cut their own evenings short to come and join us."

She went off to try to get her shopping done.

The lights flickered back on a couple of times, but went out again almost immediately. We'd all prefer to know one way or another if we're going to be without electricity for the rest of the day. If that's the case, then we might as well go home and stop wasting our time on a Friday afternoon.

Just before lunch, one of the neighbourhood watch guards who'd apprehended the criminals responsible for the theft of our computers arrived to speak to Larry. It was a very strange and complex tale. The 'fence' who was to take possession of the stolen property had accused the guards of having assaulted him and also of stealing from him. The police were now investigating the guards, instead of the fence who'd already been fingered by the two thieves currently in custody.

Larry took the guard, who had behaved so responsibly in conducting his citizen's arrest, to the Central Investigation Department in the CABS building. They went to Room 312, one of the offices in the store-breaking section.

I was extremely worried, particularly because it was Friday afternoon. If the police want to make things difficult for someone, Friday afternoon is always the time they choose. Innocent or guilty, that person will spend the weekend in the cells.

I felt sick when Larry phoned and said that he'd been told to go to Room 71 at the Central Police Station. "Just so that you know where to come to fetch the body, if necessary," he said.

I thought of Winston being taken to Room 101 in "Nineteen Eighty-Four".

> "'You asked me once,' said O'Brien, 'what was in Room
> 101. I told you that you knew the answer already. Everyone
> knows it. The thing that is in Room 101 is the worst thing in
> the world...'
>   '... In your case,' said O'Brien, 'the worst thing happens to
> be rats...'"

In my case it's a dark, windowless police cell.

What would the worst thing be for Larry?

I reckon a police cell would feature pretty high on his list, too.

A few months ago (being a good citizen), he reported a possible theft to the police. They phoned him at home two or three hours later, and insisted that he come in person to Central. He was questioned in a hostile manner by a police constable, who refused to believe his report about the calendars that were being sold on the street outside our office. They treated him as though he were guilty of some crime.

That was a Friday evening.

I didn't have to call our lawyer, thank God. He came back within half an hour. Both he and the guard had been well treated, since the police sergeant who had dealt with the original case - someone Larry knew personally – happened to be at the station. He promised to sort things out.

We left the gloomy, silent factory and went for a walk in the late afternoon sunshine to clear the cobwebs from our heads.

LEAVING?

In February Sean left to start a new life in the UK. It isn't the first time he's left Zimbabwe to test the waters elsewhere. We know he won't come back this time, because he's finally given up on Zimbabwe and on Africa.

"These fucking people," he would say furiously, "how can they watch other motorists blatantly going through red lights without even hooting. I yelled, swore, hooted and gave one of these ass-holes the finger when he cut across the vehicle ahead of me. But the wimp in the car in front didn't turn a hair. No reaction at all. He just carried on as if nothing had happened. There's absolutely no sense of outrage. How they can put up with this crap?

You're right, Dad. There's no discipline. No one seems to care about obeying the law. When last did we see a policeman walking the beat? The only police presence is at roadblocks where licences are checked or speeding tickets issued. When government dignitaries come to town, then, suddenly, there are police at every intersection. Where are the police when houses are broken into and families are tied up while jewellery, cash, TVs and videos are stolen?"

Our boy had become a very angry young man. He would never have been able to afford a car of his own, let alone a house if he'd stayed.

"Africa is no longer a place for whites. Perhaps the blacks were better off under our nasty, paternalistic colonial rule, after all. They're anything but free now. They're systematically and ruthlessly being shoved backwards by their own government."

So he left to join his less idealistic younger brother, who'd settled in London some years before. Within a couple of months, the two of them had saved enough to buy a television, a sophisticated sound system and furniture for their flat.

Colleen and Liam had settled happily in the west of Ireland. "We feel so free already," Colleen wrote after only a week, "since the albatross has been lifted from our shoulders. We look forward now to the rest of our lives and to having the liberty to shout to the winds and the sea, without looking over our shoulders, what we feel about 'YOU KNOW WHO'!"

It had been nearly two months before Diana made contact with us. We were beginning to wonder what had happened and whether she was all right. She had wept when she left her friends, her family in Durban and so many years of her life behind. With her went one crate, which was all she had to show for her life in Zimbabwe.

But when she finally wrote she was full of enthusiasm for the future.

"I heard on Friday that I'm to be offered 'sheltered housing' where I can live independently in a communal unit with assistance if necessary. Ealing is wonderful for shopping and walks. I'm learning to use buses and tubes again and had a glorious two days up in the West End – Andrea and I went off to celebrate my being declared a British citizen again and we ate in China Town. The snow was falling on the orange lanterns hanging across the street..."

Cheryl had just started working for Bulawayo Help Network, an organisation formed to co-ordinate the city's many charitable associations. Bulawayo Help was setting up a database to monitor pensioners, who might require assistance. There was, of course, no relief available from the more-or-less defunct Department of Social Welfare. Fortunately, Bulawayo people were caring and community-oriented.

Cheryl had told us at a recent Book Club meeting that often the elderly, whose children had emigrated, were too proud to admit to them that they were destitute. They would tell them that they were "fine". The Network would often have to step in and inform these relatives that their parents were anything but "fine".

"There are so many lonely old people who are in need of comfort and companionship," she told us. "They'd just like to have someone to talk to. Everyone is so busy, though. I do try to visit two or three as often as I can, but know that I'm just skimming the surface."

"You'd be surprised," she went on, "at the number of widows, who are completely clueless about things we'd take for granted. Their husbands did everything for them: from paying the bills to driving them about; from changing a light bulb to licensing a vehicle. They can't cope. Another problem is the prevalence of widows with dependant adult children, who are challenged in some way. These 'children' might have cerebral palsy, autism or Down syndrome. Their life expectancy has increased dramatically, and they could outlive their mothers. Where then would the money come from to feed and clothe them? Who would care for them and love them?"

Yvonne had agreed, "That's absolutely true. The worst nightmare of a mother, who has one of these children, is that she'll die first. What care-giver, however committed, could give her beloved, vulnerable child the same attention?"

I wondered how many of us would have left Zimbabwe by the end of the year. I would find myself speculating about each of our Book Club members. Mary would probably leave. She, Mark and their sons were young enough to be accepted as immigrants to Australia or New Zealand. Mark had always wanted to farm, and would, obviously, never realise his dream here.

Yvonne would stay, I thought, as would Cheryl. Stella and Terry would definitely fight on. Terry once told me that he could never leave Zimbabwe. "I look forward to sitting on my veranda each evening to watch the sunset," he'd said. "I'll have a couple of beers to unwind. By the time the beautiful colours have faded with the approach of dusk, I'm relaxed. That's when I feel close to God and thankful for my life here."

Women hated the lack of security and the constant uncertainty. The men refused to give up. They persisted in "making a plan". I'd often heard it said that the whites' ability to "make a plan" had contributed to our precarious situation in Zimbabwe. If we would just allow everything to fall apart completely without solving problems or finding solutions; if we would just let the wheels fall off finally instead of patching things up, then the inevitable crunch would come more quickly. But how could you stop trying if your very livelihood was at stake? How could you behave passively if people depended on you for their jobs? Not only the people you employed, but also all those who benefited indirectly – the extended families?

Moira already had a Plan B, although she didn't exactly call it that. She and Colin had bought a beach home on South Africa's South Coast. Colin could, no doubt, take early retirement. Margaret and Matthew owned their flat in Umhlanga Rocks. Margaret had often told me that the worst thing for her was being in the dark - the consequence of the incessant power cuts. They might elect to spend winters in South Africa and summers in Bulawayo.

Shirley would find herself trapped here, I thought. James thrived on the traditional Zimbabwean way of life that many, if not most, white men embraced. This entailed having drinks with 'the boys' at the pub or sports club after work; braais at the weekend; cycling and gym; fishing on the Zambezi as often as possible and watching rugby and cricket. And gardening. He was always on the go. Shirley's hobbies were reading, painting and knitting.

I hated shopping with a passion. Every week, I put it off for as long as possible. I loathed spending ridiculous sums of money on ordinary and necessary foodstuffs and cleaning materials. I resented feeling guilty when the cashier totalled my purchases, because I knew that what I had bought was likely to amount to much more than his monthly salary.

"Have a nice day," my till slip said this Saturday. I'd never noticed the message before. I was aware of it this time, because I was in the kitchen checking off my groceries against the slip.

"I can't have spent $31,346,000," I thought, horrified. "It's absolutely crazy. There must be a mistake."

There was no error, however. Each week, prices rocketed upwards. This was why I'd bought five packets of soap powder, two boxes of tissues (each costing $1,650,000) and four tiny tins of tomato paste (each $285,000). The 10kg bag of meal I'd bought for Dex cost over $7,000,000.

Before going to Solomon's, I'd visited Lavender Bay, an attractive and tastefully arranged gift shop at the Ascot Centre, to buy a cushion. The lovely girl who owned it told me that she was selling the business.

"I *have* to leave," she said. "I'm in such a rut. My friends have all gone. I need to make a new life and meet new people. I want to get married and have a family."

She was absolutely gorgeous.

Her mother, who worked with her in the shop, didn't say a word. She simply handed me my cushion with a wan smile.

I turned sixty this month. At sixty, you had to admit, finally, that you were no longer invincible.

At sixty, you were, actually, rather ancient.

CURRENCY "REDENOMINATED": TUESDAY, 1 AUGUST.

We were overwhelmed by confusion and exasperation this week, as the measures announced by the Governor of the Reserve Bank, Gideon Gono, to revalue or reclassify our inflated and impossibly unwieldy currency hit every sector of the community with brutal force. We had known that Mr Gono planned to knock three zeroes off, but no one had any idea how this was to be implemented.

Governor Gono "unveiled" the procedures he intended to put in place at a Reserve Bank presentation of his Mid-Term Monetary Policy on Monday, 31 July. ZTV broadcast his speech "live" and the government newspapers carried the information the following day in a series of articles and notices. To the man in the street (who found himself grappling all week with the fall-out) there didn't appear to have been any meaningful deliberation with the business community and professional accounting bodies, although Governor Gono listed "the stakeholders" the Reserve Bank had consulted. The public certainly had not been prepared in any way for Mr Gono's "Project Sunrise: A new beginning for Zimbabwe". (Amazing the number of people who were about to usher in this brave new "beginning".)

Mr Gono announced that a "new family" of thirteen bearer cheques issued by the Reserve Bank as a temporary form of currency was to be introduced. These bearer cheques ranged from one cent to one hundred thousand dollars. People with huge sums of bearer cheques to dispose of in the old currency would be required to produce proof of the source of the money where the funds involved were in excess of $100 million for individuals and $5 billion for companies. Where such proof was unavailable, the funds would be confiscated and deposited into Anti-Money Laundering Zero Coupon Bonds for two years. The owner of the cash would hold the bonds pending investigation and clearance with ZIMRA,[27] after which they would be redeemed at face value. Those able to prove their funds to be legitimate after they were locked up in the bonds would receive interest at the prevailing Treasury Bill rates. Daily cash withdrawals were to be limited to $100,000 for individuals and $750,000 for companies in an attempt to "curtail money laundering and parallel foreign exchange activities".

Governor Gono said that at least $35 trillion was in the hands of speculators both in the country and outside our borders. He said that the days were numbered for operators of "small reserve banks" in homes, illegal foreign currency dealers, smugglers of precious metals, those who diverted free funds intended for Zimbabwe and those who diverted inputs into "grey markets". The Central Bank, with assistance from the Ministry of Home Affairs, the Zimbabwe Revenue Authority and other relevant arms of government would descend heavily upon such offenders.

Tuesday was a nightmare. Many businesses stopped trading, so that their managers could ascertain what was required. Retailers were thrown into a state of hopeless chaos. We heard later that staff in supermarkets spent much of that night re-pricing and re-marking every item on their shelves.

On Wednesday morning I received a text message from Marilyn: "Gideon Gono has just changed his name to 'Giden Gn' in a patriotic effort to remove three zeroes." By the afternoon the entire country seemed to be in on the joke.

We had telephoned our bank for advice the previous day. We found on the Wednesday, however, that what the official had advised us to do was incorrect. It seemed that the banks had not been briefed at all. Each bank appeared to have a different policy for the first two days following the Governor's "presentation".

The chief problem was what to do about cheques drawn in the "old" currency. On 1 August our bank accepted July cheques. The next day we were advised that July cheques and

27 ZIMRA: Zimbabwe Revenue Authority

August cheques should be banked on separate deposit slips. Our messenger went to do the banking as usual in the afternoon. Banks closed at 3pm during the week. By 5pm Robbie wasn't back. Everyone else had left work. He still hadn't returned by 5.30pm and I was beginning to get really worried. Had something happened to him? Was he lying injured somewhere?

At 5.45pm, Robbie rang the factory doorbell, perspiring visibly in spite of the cold. He'd been in bank queues the entire afternoon. The chief reason for the delay had been that he had a small cash deposit to bank: a few hundred thousand in the old currency. There were only three tellers on duty. After banking the August cheques, he'd had to join a different line, the "cash" queue, behind scores of people with huge containers of cash. Trunks were being dragged across the bank floor, along with large cardboard cartons and travel bags stuffed with old bearer cheques. It had taken him an eternity to reach the front of the queue.

Much to our annoyance, the bank had refused to accept our deposit of July cheques. These now had to be returned to the drawers and reissued in the new currency. There was no hand-over period. No cognisance was to be taken of cheques in the mail, post-dated cheques etc, etc. Potential cash flow or debt collection problems did not seem issues that the framers of "Project Sunrise" had given any thought to. Any cheques (now all to be issued in the new currency) had to have the word "Revalued" positioned either top right or bottom left on the cheque and the drawer had to sign the alteration.

A problem that immediately presented itself was what to do about our accounting systems and packages. Businesses would have to close their books on 31 July and open a new set of books on 1 August. The amount of extra work this would entail was daunting. Many businesses used Pastel as their accounting package. We found that we would have to purchase Pastel version 8 in order to affect the changeover. This would cost about $300 million (old currency). Our Pastel consultant was tearing his hair out - his clients were in a state of panic and distress - and he was rushing all over town trying to allay their fears and provide solutions.

An obvious concern was the cerebral flick-flacks we were all trying to perform to equate the old currency to the new. We had been accustomed to paying millions of dollars to buy basic commodities, and it was no joke mentally to have to knock off three zeroes and have an immediate appreciation of what something was actually worth.

One wondered about all the mistakes that would cost individuals and companies millions of dollars in the new currency. And all the scams that would successfully be pulled off while people were trying to adjust.

After the pressures and concerns of this chaotic and frustrating week, we were looking forward to Book Club.

Pauline was hosting the meeting for the first time.

Her home was like an art gallery. Her collection of paintings and sculptures, all the work of local black artists, was a powerful representation of African culture.

Women with babies on their backs were picking fluffy white cotton under sapphire skies. Three small children were sitting on a pavement eating slices of water-melon. Bright pink juice ran down their chins. One little boy was leaning forward, cheeks packed full of the large brown seeds, about to spit them at his friends. A man wearing a hat full of holes was riding a rickety bicycle loaded with wood. Old wrinkled men were sitting on the bare ground in front of their huts drinking beer.

We'd had disappointing results in the past when we'd included ethnic themes in our calendar range. We'd found that it wasn't possible to please both sectors of the market. Ironically, it was the whites who appreciated the authentically depicted traditional way of life. They loved the vibrant colours and the simple figures. Blacks preferred to see themselves as sophisticated and successful. We could have sold thousands of calendars featuring smooth dudes with Ray-Bans emerging from sleek Mercedes Benz limos.

It was a while before we got down to the business of reviewing our books. Everyone wanted to talk about the effects of the new currency.

"I loved the message I had from Econet on my cell phone," said Mary. "'Please note that while our bills have been sent out in the old currency, customer payments *will be made in the new currency* in line with currency redenomination'. No 'please' or 'we respectfully request that...' So much for customer service."

"I loathe queuing," said Jeanette. "So when I go to the ZESA office to pay my electricity bill, I simply drop my cheque attached to a copy of the bill into the wooden deposit box in the corner. I went to the box as usual, only to find the slot taped up and a notice attached to the box: 'Out of Order'!"

We all burst out laughing. ZESA was probably top of everyone's hit list – after Governor Gono.

"What I don't understand," I said, "is why people would want to hoard our local old currency. It loses value every day. What would be the point of hanging onto it? We've been hearing rumours all week that there are teams of Reserve Bank officials, ZIMRA personnel and police details out raiding businesses looking for stashes of money."

"You'd be surprised at how many people have rooms literally full, floor to ceiling, of old notes," Moira said. "Colin told me that one of his biggest wholesale customers had $46 billion in the old currency in his walk-in safe, much of this in $20,000 bills. This represents his takings for a few days – he brings in $12 billion on an average day. The police arrived, arrested him and took the lot."

"Quite true," Pauline agreed. "And this is why we're heading towards another fuel crisis. Have you noticed that no one is dealing in fuel this week? It's because of the amount of currency that dealers have to hold in cash to pay for large amounts of fuel. How does anyone account for it now, with Gono's new rules and regulations in place?"

"We must be the only country in the world with a one cent note," said Cheryl. "I wonder how much it costs to produce that ridiculous, worthless piece of paper."

"Have you seen the government's advertisement captioned 'Zero to Hero'?" I asked. "The ad says 'Restore Value in the Month of Our Heroes'. They always use football concepts in their ads. The zeroes are depicted as red-carded players being sent off the field. In an appeal to the people's patriotic spirit, they say: *'Our goal is to play in one team. The team is Zimbabwe and we are looking for some great players like you, heroes: not zeroes'.* It reminds me of the 'Victory' gin the people in 'Nineteen Eighty-Four' were encouraged to drink. They were easy to manipulate, as they lived in an alcoholic daze much of the time."

"Yes," said Stella sadly. "I saw those ads and they really infuriated me. It was the MDC that came up with the football idea originally, I'm sure. Do you remember the red cards we used to wave to indicate that ZANU PF must go? It seems a long time ago now."

"I feel sorry for people who've bought money-counting machines," Mary remarked. "What will they do with them now? Perhaps with our rate of inflation it won't be long before we have hundreds of new currency notes to count. Let's hope not, though."

We moved on, eventually, to discussing the books we had read. Mary had attempted to read "Book Book" written by Fiona Farrell, an author from New Zealand. *Our* Fiona had loved the book and had given it to us when she'd visited Bulawayo the previous month. Mary had not been able to get into it, she said, but urged us all to try it, as she'd been very busy with exam marking and probably hadn't been in the right frame of mind.

Jeanette had read "Rhubarb" by Craig Silvey, a young Australian writer. Jo had given the book to us when she'd attended Mary's Book Club some months before. "Rhubarb" had just been released in Australia and had received glowing reviews.

"*...so light of touch, so full of insight into human strategies for coping...unusual, composed and engaging...*" commented 'The Bulletin'.

"*Written with wry humour and great depth of perception, this moving and often hilarious novel is a must-read...*" said the 'Melbourne Weekly'.

Jo had settled quickly in Australia and now considered it to be "home". This was not surprising, as she was a very positive, practical person. Having made the decision to leave Zimbabwe, she and her family had moved to a small mining town in Western Australia and had got on with the job of adjusting to life as new Australians. She emailed Moira regularly, and was curious to know what we thought of "Rhubarb". I'd read it some months before and had found it strange, but I couldn't really remember much about it. Then the book had disappeared for a while. Now it had mysteriously resurfaced, and we were intrigued to hear Jeanette's views.

"This is an odd book," said Jeanette. "Inside the torrent of self-consciously arranged words is quite a good story trying to show itself. It's about a blind girl and a cellist (so reclusive he's almost autistic) and about how she draws him out. Much is made of bodily functions, which doesn't really add to its charm. The book is written, I believe, by a very young man, who is certainly talented, but whose editor has let him down."

The ladies would not be making "Rhubarb" their first choice, I was sure. We had a high regard for Jeanette's opinion.

Since Shirley had been in South Africa visiting her elderly mother, she'd been able to bring us some new books. She had bought Joanna Harris's "Gentlemen and Players" which was the best book this author had written, in Shirley's opinion.

"Even better than 'Chocolat'. Al and Glenda were the only ladies who didn't enjoy 'Chocolat', but I think you'll enjoy this book, Al. Then I bought 'The Tenth Circle' by Jodi Picoult. I love her books. She's another Anita Shreve."

We seemed to have lost track of "My Sister's Keeper", also by Jodi Picoult. Who had it? We hoped it would reappear as "Rhubarb" had done.

Shirley had also bought Patricia Cornwell's latest: "At Risk". "The main character isn't Dr Kay Scarpetta," said Shirley. "I can't remember who it is. It's a thin book with a thin story. Interestingly designed cover, though, with attractive silver foiling, but there's not much else to recommend it. I'm giving up on her from now on. I feel that her plots and characters are very one-dimensional. I found, after I'd bought it, that Exclusive Books at Rosebank Shopping Centre was having a sale. I wish I'd known before I bought the Patricia Cornwell at one of their other branches. On the sale they had a 3-in-1 Robert Crais – a trilogy of Elvis Cole stories. I couldn't resist buying that, as we all love his detective novels."

Colleen had sent me "The Boy in the Striped Pyjamas" written by John Boyne, an Irish novelist only one year older than Sean. She'd loved it. It came highly recommended by her Book Group in Ireland. I'd read it three months before and had been very impressed. The publishers had deliberately refrained from summarising the book on the dust jacket, which was most unusual. They'd said that to do so would be to spoil the impact of the story. I fully agreed with this view.

Margaret did not and had told me in an e-mail that she felt it was all hype, a ploy to make the book seem more intriguing than it actually was. She felt that the story was flimsy and predictable and not really thought-provoking. She commented rather sternly: "The issues in this book don't really lend themselves to discussion. Not like 'White Lightning'. Good books should provoke intelligent, diverse discussion. Sorry, but I feel strongly about what makes good literature."

"I'm dying to know what you thought of the pyjama book, Shirl," I said.

Shirley said that she had also been unimpressed and had found the hero, a nine-year old boy, unconvincingly naïve. He must have known what was going on, she asserted.

Jeanette agreed with me. It couldn't possibly be a child's book. Children would find it deeply unsettling and horrific.

It would be great when everyone had read it. It reminded me of an extremely disturbing but brilliant book I'd read many years before called "After the First Death" by Robert Cormier. It, too, had been billed as being for children, but I felt that the issues discussed were, very definitely, adult. I had owned a copy, but must have lent it to someone who hadn't returned it. Maddening, as I now wanted to re-read it.

Pauline seemed intrigued by the controversy and I was sure that she'd make "The Boy in the Striped Pyjamas" her first choice.

Moira had been examining the metal sculptures on Pauline's walls covetously, as she was producing and directing "The Admirable Crichton". She needed primitive tools for her desert island scenes. She also had to find an old-fashioned squash box. Did anyone have one? And she needed a buck for Lady Mary to throw over her shoulder. And a grass skirt.

"You really should have brought back that kudu," said Cheryl.

Moira grimaced. "You've no idea how many other people have said the same thing."

"There's a delightful film on TV at the moment about J.M. Barrie called 'Finding Neverland'," said Stella. "I loved Peter Pan when I was a child and read 'Peter and Wendy' to my two when they were younger. Johnny Depp plays Barrie. What a gorgeous man he is!"

"I thought, at first, when I saw the title in my TV guide that it was about Michael Jackson," said Shirley. "I haven't seen the film yet, as it always seems to coincide with rugby, cycling, cricket or the world's strongest man competition. I simply hand over the remote when James comes home. I haven't the energy to argue these days. I'll watch it one morning, though."

Mary and I drove home together feeling refreshed. We felt that we could cope more positively with the second week of the ludicrous, but troubling "currency redenominated" saga.

PASS THE PARCEL

8 August

"It's like pass the parcel!" Stella said yesterday when she came in to work on some leaflets. "When the music stops, who has the money? The new buzzword is 'off-load'. You have to 'off-load' your old currency as quickly as possible, so that you don't get caught with money that's worthless."

We'd heard that our Medical Aid Society had been forced to re-issue four thousand cheques that they'd processed at the end of July in the old currency. The delay would mean we'd all have to wait longer than usual for our medical claims to be settled. Nikki, in particular, was relying on her medical aid payment to come through.

All last week, we'd heard about huge spending sprees by the wealthy elite involving vast stockpiles of money in the old currency that were being "off-loaded". Furniture, electrical appliances, cars and livestock were among the items they were buying as assets.

We'd heard stories about enterprising cashiers, who, in Aladdin-like scenarios, exchanged old notes for new, charging a fee for the transaction.

Some of the craziest stories we'd heard concerned the numerous roadblocks that had been set up to catch those trying to off-load the cash they'd stashed. These roadblocks both in towns and city centres and out on the open roads leading to the various borders were being manned by "green bombers"[28] (the Border Gezi youth militia) as well as by police and Reserve Bank officials. Rumour had it that you could possibly get through if you took a couple of "bricks" of money and threw them onto the grass verges as bribes.

"Muckraker" said in the "Zimbabwe Independent":

---

28 The youth militia are dubbed the 'Green Bombers' because they wear green drill trousers. Comparable to the Hitler Youth, they act with impunity, beating up anyone who disputes their authority.

"...Amidst the orgy of bribe-taking, cheating and intimidation of frightened and confused rural travellers we are told hungry Border Gezi youths who have no jobs were deployed to 'curb corruption'. It's a farce beyond comment."

9 August

Yesterday staff at "The Chronicle" must have been very excited.

The newspaper's headline blared: *"$500 billion recovered – 2,545 arrested for money laundering."* The writer of the article explained that the Reserve Bank had estimated that only $15 trillion out of the $43 trillion on the market was circulating in the formal economy. The bank suspected that between $10 trillion and $15 trillion had been smuggled out of the country. It also had *"reason to believe"* that trillions of dollars were in the hands of illegal foreign currency dealers.

10 August

"The Chronicle" was more excited than it had been on Tuesday. It had an even bigger scoop.

"The Reserve Bank of Zimbabwe and security agents yesterday recovered more than $10 trillion, the biggest haul since the launch of eight-day-old Operation Sunrise/Ilanga Seliphumile."

What an incredible amount of money even in these hyper-inflationary times. We're all dying to find out who's been stashing it away.

11 August

Everyone was chuckling yesterday.

A large proportion of the massive haul - that triumph for Operation Sunrise - has turned out to be cash in transit belonging to Barclays Bank and FBC Bank. Spokespersons from the two banks said there was nothing unusual in their movement of large amounts of cash. Money had to be transferred from one centre to another in the course of "normal banking practice".

This explanation didn't mollify Police Commissioner, Augustine Chihuri, though. The financial institutions should apologise. "They have a lot of explaining to do, especially to the nation, including the President himself," he's reported to have said.

We loved the headline in "The Chronicle".

"Inflation rate goes down".

16 August

Patrick returned from his long weekend in Mutare with tales of the eleven roadblocks he and the other passengers on their bus had had to pass through. At each roadblock everyone's luggage was taken down from the roof rack and searched. Then the bus itself was virtually taken apart so that every conceivable nook and cranny could be examined. Finally, each person had to be checked for hidden bundles of old notes. The forces of "law and order" meant business.

Towards the end of last week there was a rumour that fake bearer cheques in the new currency were circulating. The Zimbabwe bird watermark was missing on some of the new notes. Further investigation revealed that such notes were indeed in circulation, but that they were not fakes. Something had "gone wrong" with the printing process. These would be regarded as acceptable currency, but should be returned to the Reserve Bank.

19 August

Laura has found some fuel at last. She's been having problems sourcing both petrol and diesel in Harare, which, as always, we have to pay for in cash. Black market dealers are the only option – there's been nothing available from legitimate suppliers for ages.

With road blocks and police checkpoints set up all over town, she was even more nervous than usual. In the past, she's had to take two large sports bags to the bank and she's needed either Steph or Arnold to go with her to help carry the loot. On this occasion, she set off alone with a cash cheque for

$250 thousand ($250 million in the old currency) and a small, compact container in which to carry the new currency.

When she arrived at the bank (having arranged the transaction well in advance), she was told that most of the cash would have to be in the old currency and that she could have only $100 thousand in the new currency, since there were insufficient new notes available.

So she'd filled the little container to bursting point and then stuffed the rest of the money down her trousers and into the pockets of her jacket. She'd waddled pregnantly out of the bank, rustling like a tree blowing in the wind. Much to her relief she wasn't stopped and searched on her way back to the office. She was glad, too, she said, that the old notes were in mint condition, since some had found their way into her knickers.

Special Places

Pauline was a brilliant mathematician and a gifted teacher. Fourteen years before, when my boys were at school, maths and science teachers had been, even then, very difficult to recruit. Most had left education for better paid jobs in commerce or industry. Now they must be almost extinct. Pauline, herself, had left the formal and limited world of the classroom, and tutored pupils at home. She was patient but firm and had the reputation of being able to achieve miracles with struggling and confused students.

We were listening to her speak of a workshop she had initiated. She often attended book launches and art exhibitions and was very interested in promoting promising new authors and poets. On one such occasion recently, a young black author had been invited to read an excerpt from a story he had written entitled "My Special Place". He spoke eloquently of a special place and a special woman. His special woman wanted nothing to do with tradition. She spurned the idea of lobola[29] and of women being treated as possessions by male family members.

Pauline had been intrigued. How did educated young black girls in today's Zimbabwe feel about this crucial issue? Would they discuss the subject freely in the presence of a white woman?

She organised a small group of black teenage girls and invited them to her home. She felt that they would be able to relax more easily in an informal setting. The young author read his story, this time expanding on his relationship with the woman he loved. Afterwards Pauline asked the girls to close their eyes and think of their own "special place".

"Then," Pauline said, "they spent ten minutes or so writing about this place. The results were amazing. What they wrote

29 Lobola: Payments made by the bridegroom to his future father-in-law.

was beautiful and very individual. One of the girls said that her special place was the beach. I found this surprising, as there can't be many young black Zimbabweans who've experienced seaside holidays."

"It was a fascinating afternoon. We could have gone on for hours. The girls all wanted a different life for themselves. They hated the idea of being bought and sold like cattle. They wanted loving husbands, equality within the home, and, needless to say, the right to bring up their own daughters as empowered persons. "

Pauline's eyes sparkled with enthusiasm as she talked. What an asset to Book Club she was, I thought. She'd been with us only a few months, and she'd already changed the dynamics of the group with her energy and exciting new ideas.

Stella, too, was in an exuberant mood.

"I've just spent a day out in a remote rural area," she said. "My mandate was to discuss health care. I was very nervous, as I wasn't sure how receptive the people would be to someone speaking English - a language few would understand. Once again, I was the only white person present. But I needn't have worried. My interpreter did a great job. Everyone listened attentively, and, when I had finished outlining our plans for improved health facilities, they clapped and cheered."

"They demand so little, you know. They just want food, shelter, medical care and education for their families. The absolute basics. And they also want democracy. They haven't given up. I shook many hands and answered all sorts of questions."

"I came back feeling humbled and uplifted. We complain so much here in town. Out there they have so little and yet there was a sense of joyous approval for what Arthur is trying to achieve. Our mission is to reach rural folk countrywide to let them know that we care about them and that they have a voice."

How many other white women would do what Stella was doing?

Trudy Stevenson[30], Heather Bennett[31], Kerry Kay and Jenny Coltart would. But not many others.

Since all of us except Stella had read "The Boy in the Striped Pyjamas", we felt that we could finally discuss the plot. Pauline had reminded us at Yvonne's Book Club that the book's jacket indicated that the story should be viewed as a "fable". Most of the girls agreed that the book was a metaphor, intended to outline the consequences of extreme racism and prejudice. Retribution and punishment were exacted in the most horrific and yet appropriately just fashion. In this regard, the book was very satisfying. It should not be taken too literally, they felt. It was a classic case of the sins of the fathers being visited upon the children. It had overtones of Greek tragedies and morality plays. The value of the book lay in the fact that it forced you to think about the issues long after you had finished reading it. It was deceptively simplistic.

I felt that the book jolted the reader into a state of shocked awareness. One was called upon to examine one's own behaviour at every level. Children were innocents, often exploited and made to suffer by unscrupulous adults. I did not see this young boy as extraordinarily naïve. I saw him as the archetypal innocent victim of the mayhem brought about by self-serving, power-hungry adults. He was not merely the universal child, however. His character was developed cleverly, he was a real person, often selfish and self-engrossed. And he had many endearing qualities.

Pauline told us that she had asked her friend, the young author, to read and comment on the book. He had found it so worthwhile, she said, that he had taken the time to write down some of his thoughts.

30 Trudy Stevenson: a founding member of the MDC and the first white woman to be voted onto the MDC's National Executive. She was elected to parliament in 2000.
31 Heather Bennett: wife of Roy Bennett, who won a strong victory in the Chimanimani constituency in the 2000 general election. During the election campaign, Heather, who was 5 months pregnant, was physically abused by ZANU activists on their farm and subsequently lost her baby.

'The central idea, I think, is that whenever we perceive others as being different from us, we will reap nothing but sorrow... Every time we harm someone for whatever reason, we harm ourselves. Whenever we express the base, we deny the sublime that exists in each one of us...

The story explores the theme of limitation, and limitation is universal. Humanity universally limits itself horribly with catastrophic effects. We limit ourselves to nationalistic and racial boundaries and refuse to celebrate the universal truths that bind us - such as our love of beauty, peace and success. We desire these only for ourselves and for those like us, refusing to see the humanity of the "other" be he black, Jewish or Palestinian...

What happened in Germany was not an event in isolation. Today, three-quarters of the world's population starves, while one quarter consumes three-quarters of our global resources. This too is a holocaust. We cannot be indifferent to one another. We have to learn to love one another unconditionally..."

What an intelligent and thoughtful young man.

"If you read only one book this month, Stels," I said, "read this one. No matter how exhausted you are, this book will keep you awake. I guarantee you won't be able to put it down."

We'd read several books lately about children caught in webs of horror and fear. I had just finished reading "Ghost Girl" by Torey Hayden and we'd read two books about street children, one white and one black. Many of us were looking forward to reading "My Sister's Keeper". I'd noticed lately that authors were writing about the protective love that fathers felt for their children. Gone was the old-fashioned notion that fathers should have little to do with the exacting task of rearing children. Women were often portrayed by modern writers as the guilty party in the marriage – *they* had the affairs or left their young children irresponsibly and the men picked up the pieces, did the cooking and got their children to school every day, clean and on time.

I found myself lying awake in the early hours of Sunday morning, thinking about *my* special place. Of all the places I loved in Zimbabwe, Inyanga (now renamed Nyanga) was the most special. I was twelve years old when I visited the Eastern Districts for the first time.

"The woods are lovely dark and deep..."
High in the woods, far from the cottage, we leaned against the trunks of three pine trees. Hundreds reached upward, their branches filtering the shafts of sunlight. The distilled glow that came through to us had a warm, gentle, amber radiance. Layer upon layer of spongy brown pine needles formed a luxuriant carpet into which we sank as we moved. We breathed in the fresh, minty air and were content.

The farm had been sold. Saying goodbye to our loveable, placid cattle, the river where we had fished so often, the lands where we had grown tobacco, maize and sorghum, the baobab tree, and to all our precious, secret places had not been easy. We were moving to Marandellas. Friends had lent us their holiday cottage at Juliasdale for two months, while our house was being built.

Glyn and I had saved up and had bought a wind-up gramophone, lots of spare needles and several records – the very latest hits. While we practised dance steps to "Mona Lisa", "Seven Little Girls' and "Itsy Bitsy Teeny Weeny Yellow Polka Dot Bikini", Carl would wander off to work on his knife-throwing skills. Tree trunks provided large, obliging targets and his accuracy improved dramatically.

The cottage overlooked "The Valley of the Moon". We would watch the rain coming towards us in misty curtains systematically blotting out each distant violet hill. Finally in a torrent of rushing sound, it would be upon us, darkening our garden, and we would see the ferns bend and hear the little stream that trickled past the house and down the hill begin to flow vigorously.

We had never experienced rain like this before. On "Solitude", from time to time, there had been heavy storms, when the river came down in flood and the farm roads had been impassable. In the Eastern Districts - Juliasdale, Inyanga and Troutbeck – we could expect days and days of soaking rain. Dense mists would enshroud the valley, cutting our garden off from the rest of the world.

The Nyangombe Falls close by were spectacular. After we had clambered down a fairly steep slope (very slippery in wet weather), the sound of roaring water urged us towards the falls. From a large, flat rock right at the edge, we could view the wide expanse of water foaming and frothing over jagged rocks. The many streamlets merged, and then tumbled down in one long drop to the river far below.

With the help of tree branches and bracken, we managed to scramble down the cliff. At the bottom, we found a sparkling, sapphire pool where tiny fish swam among the pebbles and stones. No bilharzia in *this* water. It was too cold.

We'd always been threatened with dire consequences if we swam in the Umsweswe River that ran through our farm. Its waters were riddled with bilharzia. It was almost impossible not to have contact with river water, though. When we put worms onto wet hooks or paddled across a shallow ford, we could visualise the disgusting, microscopic parasites burrowing into our skins and lodging themselves in our bodies. All our drinking water was boiled, as was our bath water. Our parents were meticulous. Although we were not as careful, we did try to avoid being contaminated by still water near reeds and water lilies.

So to be able to swim in a natural pool with a clear conscience was exhilarating. We basked in the sunlight in the centre, treading water for a while, as we watched the pounding water cascading down. Then we dried ourselves and climbed back to join our parents, who were perched on a comfortable rock near the main falls. Ravenously hungry by now, we returned to our car for a picnic lunch. Sandwiches had seldom tasted so good.

One of the highlights of our Inyanga stay was climbing Mount Nyangani. We set out early on a clear morning and allowed five or six hours for the climb. There were numerous small streams that we could drink from along the way, but it was advisable to take water with us just in case. These were instructions from the wardens manning the little rest hut at the foot of the mountain. We should, under no circumstances, undertake an afternoon climb and if, at any time, the mists came down, we were to remain wherever we were. We should not continue climbing to the summit or attempt to come down the mountain if visibility was bad. We must follow the arrows and signs and must not deviate from the path. The mountain could be treacherous – people had gone missing, they told us, never to be found again.

Our father, who was seldom well, had stayed behind at the cottage. Our mother was extremely fit, and Glyn and I struggled to keep up with her and Carl, as we worked our way in single file towards the top. She revelled in action and adventure, and we were very proud of her. Every so often, we would stop to catch our breath and look back to assess how far we had come. Narrow ribbons of silver water ran down the grey rock faces all around us. The mountain reared starkly above us. Gradually, the little hut became a tiny speck in the distance and then vanished altogether.

On we climbed, higher and higher until we reached a series of plateaux. This section was a welcome change and we finally stopped gasping for breath. Here the grass was short and scrubby and there were a few marshy areas to cross. There was another short climb, and then we found ourselves, quite suddenly, on top of Nyangani, overlooking Rhodesia to the west and Mozambique to the east. We had heard it said that on a very clear day, you could actually see the Indian Ocean. We strained our eyes, narrowing them to slits and shielding them from the glare, but we couldn't see anything other than pale blue sky. We gave up this rather futile exercise, and turned to look across our own country.

What a wonderful sensation and what a thrilling sense of achievement. There, as far as the eye could see, was a hazy mauve landscape of smaller mountains and hills and distant miniature rivers that snaked through gorges, disappeared into forests and emerged again as waterfalls. It was stunningly, breathtakingly beautiful. We were kings and queens, surveying that purple realm spread out before us.

Eventually, we had to shrug off the seductive magic of the summit and start the descent. There was no longer a mission to accomplish, no alluring, panoramic view to gaze upon, no breathless sense of anticipation. We were weary and hungry and simply wanted to get to the bottom as quickly as possible. We couldn't wait to cool off in the pool under the bridge near the Rhodes Hotel.

Tomorrow we'd rest our tired muscles on soft pine needle beds, eat freshly picked peaches and talk about the next two weeks. We wanted to see the Pungwe Falls and the Honde View, climb "The Crusader", a mountain less than three miles away and visit the Mtarazi Falls and Mare Dam. We planned to hire a boat and row across the lake at Troutbeck. On Monday we would drive down to Umtali, the closest town, to buy provisions and presents.

It would be our first Christmas away from "Solitude".

But I'd found my special place.

It is a Little Inconvenient...

17 December

Zimbabwe is no longer a place for dreams.
For months we've been agonising about our future.
We love Bulawayo. We own a business and a beautiful home.
We have friends, two cats and a dog.
Larry came out to join the BSA Police when he was twenty.
He fell in love with the country and later with me. He has
ploughed all his energy into our lives here.
This is my life. I don't know anything else.
Everything is here.

24 December

Everything *was* here.
I have to face the fact that Sean and Brian will never come
back. I have to accept that Glyn and Ian won't be driving up
from Durban to spend Christmas holidays with us anymore.
Ian can't handle the long hours travellers have to endure at the
border standing in stifling-hot, chaotic queues. Why should he
pay bribes for the routine processing of valid visas and travel
documents? And struggling to find fuel when they get here
doesn't exactly qualify as relaxation or entertainment.

27 December

Running our business is becoming impossible. We've no
access to foreign currency and this situation is not likely to
change. Not for years, anyway. Our suppliers have become
increasingly unreliable, as things get tougher for them. We
had a terrible patch last month when we couldn't get ink.
Printers without ink aren't much good to anyone. As we put
out one fire, another flares up immediately. Nothing new, of
course, especially at this time of year, but the frequency and
intensity has been alarming. Payments are becoming more
and more difficult to meet. There is no longer such a thing

as "terms". Inflation is horrific, with the dollar devaluing on a daily basis.

Diaries have been an even worse problem than usual. We're miles behind - there are still thousands to be delivered, so no year-end/Christmas shut-down for any of us this year.

I can't bear the thought of having to start the new diary cycle all over again next week. It seems crazy to begin work on the 2008 range while 2007 deliveries are still so far behind schedule.

29 December

We've given up hoping that things will get better. Indications are that 2007 will be even worse than 2006. We no longer have confidence in the MDC. They are so ineffectual. Morgan and Arthur will have to sort out their problems without our help. "Voices" seems a hundred years ago. I believed then that we could achieve something. It amazes me now that I was so naïve.

The Christmas newsletter from Safe-Home Ireland arrived yesterday. They're welcoming people home from all over the world. It's apparent that older people are looked after and valued. There's always a wealth of information about benefits; housing opportunities; travel passes; opening bank accounts; the weather; hurling and Gaelic football.

Colleen writes glowingly about their new life in County Mayo. She and Liam are having a marvellous time rediscovering their roots. They go to the theatre regularly and have joined the Heritage Society.

They belong.

3 January

We both have Irish passports.

Larry can finish the book he's writing. He'll be eligible for an Irish pension when he turns 66 later this year. I'll have to find a job. In Ireland it doesn't seem to matter if you're over 60. I have a degree, I can sell and I have production and managerial experience. I wish I'd made more effort to develop computer skills, though. Somehow, I'm going to have to remedy that. Timing is critical. If we go, it's got to be within the next two months. But we have to deliver everyone's diaries and calendars first before we look for a buyer. We cannot allow our suppliers to find out that we're planning to leave. There's a real risk that they might renege on agreements (made earlier in the year) that are no longer profitable for them. Inflation has wiped out the value of the deposits we paid. They might reason that they've got nothing to lose if we're not going to be around in 2007. And then we'll never get the rest of the diaries out to our customers.

6 January

We hate pretending that we're still committed to trying to make things work. Despite all the opposition's set-backs, Stella has never lost faith. Yesterday, she invited me to join a think-tank to consider health matters. I felt privileged to be asked, and can't bear deceiving her. As always, I'm in awe of her selflessness. She's determined to improve life-expectancy and the standard of living.

In April last year, the World Health Organisation reported that Zimbabwean women had an average life expectancy of 34 years and Zimbabwean men 37 years. Women's life expectancy had fallen by two years in the previous 12 months, they said. Our women now have the lowest life expectancy in the world. Poverty and deaths from AIDS are responsible for this dreadful situation.

22 January

We've made excellent progress during the week on the remaining diaries. Today Larry is going to approach two companies we think might be interested in buying Alfa. He'll ask them to keep our intentions confidential. We've received the final deliveries of diaries from our suppliers and none of our customers have cancelled their orders.

26 January

We've had offers from both companies. It's great that they think Alfa is worth buying. They've agreed to take on all our permanent staff. Our employees have an excellent reputation for loyalty and for their unusual work ethic. We're very proud of them.

29 January

We've sold Alfa.

Now we have to put the house on the market.

31 January

We've written to Safe-Home to tell them that we plan to leave very soon. We've got about six weeks to shut our lives down here.

We won't be able to take much with us. It's too expensive to send furniture and household effects across the world. And we've no idea what type of accommodation they'll find for us. Wherever it is, it'll be small – an awful lot smaller than this beloved house where we've lived for twenty years.

It's going to break my heart to leave behind mum's furniture – particularly the massive old wardrobe in our bedroom and the display cabinet with its leaded glass doors in the lounge. They still smell of the farm and they're all I have left of my childhood. Whenever I pull out a drawer or open a door, mum is there in the room with me.

The beautifully carved wooden chest in our hallway is known as a "kist" in South Africa and Zim. A bride traditionally stored the linen she collected for her trousseau in her kist. Mum always insisted on calling it her "camphor chest".

I love the clean, fresh, aromatic fragrance that wafts upwards when I open it. On the lid, exotic oriental figures converse with one another, while, on the front, others bringing gifts bow to a seated dignitary. Fabulous buildings and elegant bridges serve as backdrops, while swaying trees incline gracefully towards them.

I cannot leave it behind.

"I would hate you girls to have an awful mess to sort out when I die," mum often used to say. "You can't believe the clutter people here accumulate."

Glyn and I found everything in her little cottage in perfect order.

4 February

This is not the case in our house, unfortunately.

I started in Brian's room. During his photographer phase, he captured our cats in every conceivable pose. On tree branches. Asleep on his bed. Jumping for a piece of meat held out of reach. The circus trick: a kitten's head in one of the puppy's mouths. He also decided at one stage that he might like to be a drummer. He'd kept the drum sticks, in case he felt the urge again sometime. And all his tennis racquets, squash racquets, hockey sticks and tennis balls. Right at the back of the cupboard were the drawings and paintings from his college years. Every single one of them. And all the boxes from his project on packaging: some squashed flat and others gummed up with spiders' webs, dust and the odd rat dropping.

Sean's room was much worse. By this time I had learned to be ruthless. I threw out every cash slip, every unopened bank statement, every gym schedule and every party or wedding invitation. I used two or three of his gym bags for the sparring gloves, bandages, skipping ropes and spring balls. Just as well the heavy punch bag wasn't still there. The coins were valueless, since they were no longer legal tender. These went in the bin along with ancient calculators that hadn't worked for years, sunglasses that weren't Ray-Bans, penknives that weren't Leathermen, key rings with silly slogans and a surprising number of condoms. I kept all the paperclips that hadn't rusted, as these now cost a fortune if you can find them. They'll come in useful at work.

I've thrown away scores of mother's day cards, birthday cards and anniversary cards. I'd accumulated envelopes of all shapes and sizes – you never knew when they'd come in handy. I'd thought I was quite tidy - definitely not a pack-rat. Not like

Larry, whose paper trail extended from our bedroom through to the cupboards in the passage and on into the study.

How could four people amass so much rubbish?

12 February

After the bedrooms with their concealed caches of junk, I've found working in the lounge and dining room a breeze. I simply cover the floors with glassware and ornaments; set aside the stuff to be crated and pack the rest into boxes for Larry to take to the auctions.

I've had to say goodbye to many lovely things: to the heavy crystal vase Gillian and the reps gave us for Christmas one year; to the beautiful glass flutes they gave us on another occasion; to my mother's dinner service that we've seldom used; to the whiskey glasses and decanter Larry brought me from the Czech Republic. I'm trying to convince myself that these are just things that can be replaced one day in the First World. Practicality is the name of the game.

I'd kept many lovely things "for best". A "best" that has never happened. And now, it never will. Instead of planting ourselves in front of the TV night after night, I wish we'd eaten meals in our dining room more often. I wish I'd used our elegant wine glasses. I wish I'd lit the scented candles I've hoarded for years.

14 February

We've left the study till last.

There are hundreds of books and Larry has rows and rows of boxing trophies. Books are heavy and trophies take up space. Larry knows we'll never have room to display them wherever we land up in Ireland. We've decided to keep the three most significant – those he was awarded for his South African titles - and we've decided to donate the rest to Christian Brothers College. It was very hard for him to part with these mementos of his exceptionally successful amateur boxing career. I know I'm being selfish, but I'm relieved I won't have to clean and polish them. There'll be no Betty[32] in Ireland.

32 Betty: Our wonderful maid.

15 February

Which books shall we take? Larry bought our set of encyclopaedias in 1966 shortly after he joined the police. They've served us well over the years. But they're now, very definitely, obsolete. My Complete Works of Shakespeare and our dictionaries can be replaced. There's no question about our poetry books. Many are out of print. They're essentials, and so are all our Rhodesian, Zimbabwean and South African reference books. We've discarded two tomes of George Bernard Shaw's Plays and Prefaces. This hurt Larry, as he admires Shaw, and they've been extremely useful. We've also selected a few of our favourite novels. It's a bit like being asked: "Which five books would you choose to have with you, if you were marooned on a desert island?"

Larry chose "Catch 22"; a Gun Digest; "In the Ring" - a book of boxing stories; "Trinity" by Leon Uris; "Ireland – A Terrible Beauty" by Jill and Leon Uris; a large volume of "World Mythology"; "Northern Ireland – The Orange State" and "The Small Dark Man" and "The Key Above the Door" by Maurice Walsh. I selected "In this House of Brede" (the first book I reviewed for Book Club so many years ago); "The Complete Book of Flower Fairies" by Cecily Mary Barker; two copies of "To Kill a Mockingbird" (I've always had two copies in case one goes missing); "The Siege of Krishnapur"; "Skallagrigg" by William Horwood; "Nineteen Eighty-Four"; "The Great Gatsby"; "Anne of Green Gables" and "Anne of Avonlea".

Larry carted piles of books to CBC and The Gallery and the rest to the auctions. We try to ignore the dusty, empty bookcases.

We had printouts of ZW News stacked in piles all over the study along with MDC information and reference material we'd used for "Voices". We've torn everything into small pieces, as we don't want to be hauled off to Bulawayo Central to be interrogated about the possession of subversive literature just as we're leaving.

We're not planning to emigrate officially. It'll be less complicated to "go on holiday".

I've been agonising about whether to take some of my teaching notes and handouts with me. It's tempting to ditch the lot. I'm not planning to teach again after twenty-three years, but who knows? Yet I invested so much time, thought and effort in "Was Hamlet Mad?", "The Difference between Tragedy and Pathos" and on the passages I used for literary criticism.

I've decided to select the more significant exercises. They can go in the camphor chest along with photo albums, loose photos, scrapbooks and certificates. There are also thousands of recipes to sort through. Obviously I'll never get round to trying them all in this lifetime. In the evenings, when I've had enough of tearing up paper, I watch TV with one eye and copy out interesting-looking recipes into an exercise book. The ingredients for some of the more unusual will be available in Ireland. I won't have to improvise any longer.

19 February

Our pictures are originals, all with a flavour of Africa. We know most of the artists personally. This has been one of the perks of owning a company that produces calendars. We have four of Sally Jones' scenic paintings done in oils and one of a charging elephant in pastels. I particularly love her corrugated Nyanga road lined with gum trees. We have ethnic rural scenes, owls, guinea fowls, flowers and a portrait of a regal Matabele warrior. There are several animal paintings done in mixed media by Elva Palombo, who emigrated some years ago. Larry's favourite is a group of painted dogs lit by a ghostly moon. Behind them are leaping buck - shadowy bushman paintings come alive. We have two superb water colours by Douglas Tannahill, a Harare artist, originally from Northern Ireland. Alan Winter painted The Crusader Mountain for us. It's the view from the window of our honeymoon hotel.

Each picture has its story and its special place in our hearts. We can't take them all.

22 February
I cry while I pack. I cry when I throw away old letters. I cry when Dexter follows me round the garden, nuzzling me lovingly, or when Mission and Olly purr beside me trustingly on the couch. I cry when I tell Betty how special she is and how much I will miss her.

I cry as the house gradually becomes an empty shell.

I cannot stop crying.

1 March
Saying goodbye to everyone at work yesterday was even worse.

We both cried.

4 March
My last Book Club was at Yvonne's house at Malachite Park.

I was there and I wasn't there.

I was at Veronica's house in Hillside on that day long ago when we'd started this Book Club. I'd wanted to be the best mother in the world and I'd wanted some time to myself... I was in Rachel's house on the day we'd defined our objectives and gone our separate ways... It was the first Saturday in December, and already there was a whiff of magic in the air. Margaret's dining table was decorated with candles, roses and pine cones and she'd made mince pies and Christmas cake... I was at Cheryl's on a cold winter morning stroking a grey cat lying beside me on the sofa. A fire warmed the room and the smell of coffee drifted in from the kitchen... I was at Mary's house. We were discussing "Crow Lake". It was Jo's last Book Club before she left for Australia. Had she, too, felt this hollow sense of unreality?

I don't remember any of the reviews.

I do remember looking at each person and wondering whether I'd ever see her again.

Jonathan reminded his mother several times that he was hungry. Yvonne spoke firmly and lovingly to him. This was a meeting for grown-ups. She was sure he could be tidying his bedroom, or making himself useful in some other way.

I was there and I wasn't there.

Finally, it was time to leave.

"We're going to miss you," they told me. "It's not going to be easy to replace you." They gave me a set of linen placemats and napkins with beautifully beaded napkin rings. "Something easy to pack," they said. "Don't forget us."

20 March

I want to wrap the house and garden around me like a blanket.

I don't want to go to the Matopos one last time. Neither does Larry. We don't want farewell parties, dinners and lunches. We want to be cocooned until we have to close the gate for the last time and leave for the airport.

23 March

We think we may have sold the house. People have traipsed in and out for weeks. One of the estate agents has a thing about linen cupboards. She gets excited because we've got two.

I'm happy when prospective buyers say what a lovely garden we have and what a relief it would be to have a good borehole.

29 March

Dex jumped eagerly into Bonnie's car. He teetered about in the back of the old station wagon, making it wobble violently. Perhaps he should jump into the front seat with the nice lady? Saliva flew everywhere, as he shook his head vigorously, slobbering excitedly. Bonnie just laughed good-naturedly. She's our vet and has several large dogs of her own. A Great Dane would be a welcome addition, she'd said. No criminal in his right mind would trespass on her property.

Dex didn't look back, as they drove away.

Some weeks ago Cheryl generously offered to have Mission and Olly. Although she has several other cats, she loves animals and is quite relaxed about having two more. Typically, they didn't come when we called them, so we had to search the house and garden and hope that Olly hadn't gone walkabout. Eventually, we found them sleeping peacefully under a bush. Scooping them up, we thrust them into the cat cage and fastened the door, before they realised what was happening. After a brief, irritable spat in their cramped quarters, they settled down. Unlike Dexter, they hate cars and we knew they'd complain piteously all the way to their new home.

Tomorrow it will be our turn.

Two days ago we received an email from Safe-Home.

"Hi, you two
We have a definite offer of housing for you in County Wexford. It should be ready for you to walk into, as it's part furnished. It's a two bedroom, two storey house. We will arrange for someone to meet you in Dublin, and she will drive you to your new home.
Regards and travel safely
Mary Ann, Safe-Home Ireland."

Epilogue: Departure Call

We are pleased to announce the departure of South African Airways Flight SA 0337 to London, Heathrow. Will all passengers travelling on this flight make their way through customs and immigration to complete departure formalities. I repeat, will all passengers travelling on South African Airways Flight SA 0337 to London, Heathrow...

The red dust boiled and swirled behind the old cattle truck. Mum and Dad were remote in the small isolated world of the front cab. We three children, standing at the back in the glorious afternoon sunshine, savoured the familiar landmarks as we rattled and shuddered over the corrugations.

It had been a long term. Boarding school was not for the faint-hearted. One of the worst aspects was the food. Oatmeal porridge, greyish glue with large lumps, was Glyn's personal hell. Boiled eggs could be too soft with the whites runny, or rock-hard with the beginnings of life evident. Carl once found a fish hook in a plate of macaroni cheese. My absolute worst was boiled leeks. The teacher on duty would insist that everything on one's plate had to be finished. Dropping food on the floor "by mistake" didn't work. You would be given another helping and required to eat it no matter how long it took. It was torture.

Soon we would be eating roast chicken oozing with succulent stuffing and heaping our plates with home-grown pumpkin, peas and potatoes. We would explore the kitchen cupboards and find tins of our mother's delicious biscuits dripping with pink icing and decorated with silver balls or hundreds and thousands and containers packed full of her home-made fudge, caramels and Turkish delight. Soon we would be wandering through the lands inspecting the maize and tobacco and walking with the dogs by the river. We could spend the afternoons fishing or reading, we could watch the cattle being dipped, we could soak up the sunshine and run laughing through the rain.

This is a second call for all passengers travelling on South African Airways Flight SA 0337 to London, Heathrow. Please make your way through customs and immigration to complete exit formalities.

Our teenage years in Marandellas vibrated with music, dancing and many friends. The school holidays were brim-full of mornings at the swimming pool, followed by lazy afternoons in our favourite café drinking coke-floats and feeding the juke box.

Maureen's mother was easy-going. Each weekend she would put up with crowds of noisy teenagers who ate all her biscuits and drank gallons of her homemade lemonade. In her garden, under the msasa trees, we would play the latest hits and practise our dance steps for the next party.

Will all passengers travelling to London, Heathrow on South African Airways Flight SA 0337 make their way down Route 5. Passengers will be departing through Gate 27 in 30 minutes.

I was talking to Elizabeth when John ran upstairs to tell me that my visitor had arrived. I was very nervous. Blind dates were awful. I wouldn't like him; he'd be shorter than me and his conversation would be limited to recounting sagas of his drinking prowess. He'd be disappointed because I wasn't beautiful and didn't have long, flowing hair and Raquel Welch's figure. So I entered the apartment cautiously, with my knees wobbling and without the faintest idea of how to start the conversation. He rose to greet me and I felt a surge of relief. He was wearing a tracksuit in the national colours with the Rhodesian badge and the word "Boxing" underneath. I loved sport. Wow, what a bonus!

We found that we had much in common: a love of literature, movies and music. He introduced me to "The Rubaiyat" of Omar Khayyam, to Robert Service's "The Shooting of Dan McGrew" and "The Cremation of Sam McGee" and to Yeats' beautiful "Host of the Air". He read me the whole of "The

Small Dark Man" during our magical honeymoon in the Eastern Highlands.

Departure call for passengers travelling to London, Heathrow. Will all passengers make their way to Gate 27. This flight is now boarding.

We used to take Sean and Brian to the drive-in cinema often. They loved these outings. On balmy nights we would gather up blankets, pillows, cool drinks, liquorice allsorts and crisps and join the rows of cars to watch such favourites as "King Kong", "Gold Finger" and "Grease". At interval there were jungle gyms and slides to play on.

"King Kong" was the boys' extra special movie, to be superseded only by "Star Wars" years later. We will never forget the first time we all saw it. Jessica Lange was tied up, a forlorn, frail figure, awaiting her fate. Thunderous steps could be heard approaching. Boom, boom, boom. The ground trembled and shuddered. Suspense and tension mounted. The boys crouched on the back seat of the car, eyes riveted, hands clenched in anticipation. Boom, boom, boom. King Kong stomped into view, a terrifying presence.

"Stick 'em up, you guys!" Brian said in a grim voice.

We still laugh every time we remember our little boy's quirky humour.

All passengers for South African Airways Flight SA 0337 to London, Heathrow are to make their way to Gate 27. This flight is now boarding.

There have been many New Years – parties, dinners and dances at clubs, hotels and private homes. The most memorable was our New Year at Big Cave in the Matopos. After an excellent dinner, we wondered how our hosts would entertain us. Staying at the lodge were people of different ages from all over the world. It would not be easy.

Dave announced that we would be going out in the trucks on a game drive. This would be a unique experience for many of the foreign visitors. We saw several sable, three wildebeest, a small herd of impala and an owl or two that, disturbed by the sound of the trucks, flew off screeching into the night. The anticipation was more of an adrenaline rush than the sightings. At any moment something might materialise from the darkness and confront us.

We emerged from the bush. In a clearing, lanterns hung from the branches of two or three trees and chairs had been arranged in a circle. Fires burning in braziers took the chill off the night. We sipped liqueurs: Baileys, Amarula and Cape Velvet; listened to the sounds just outside our enchanted moonlit circle and talked quietly, almost reverently.

"In such a night," I thought, "in such a night as this, it's hard to believe that Zimbabwe is in a state of crisis. In such a night only beauty is relevant. On other nights in other places and at other times we must remember and be thankful..."

Reluctantly, we climbed into the trucks, and were driven back to the lodge. We found the big cave itself lit up with festive lanterns and another welcoming fire burning at the entrance. We toasted marshmallows and warmed ourselves with more liqueurs and coffee. We were celebrating the end of 2001 and welcoming in the New Year of 2002.

This is the final call to all passengers travelling to London, Heathrow on South African Airways Flight SA 0337. Gate 27 is now closing.

An evening spin in Matthew's motorboat is a wonderful conclusion to the long, hot journey from Bulawayo to Olive Beadle Fishing Camp on the Zambezi. The river is vast, a huge expanse of serene, blue water. Hills rise up on the Zambian side, hazed with dry, brown brush. Wizened baobabs sprouting ungainly limb-like branches cling to the sparse, rocky earth. We ease into reedy inlets looking for suitable fishing spots. Then we speed upriver to feel the wind on our faces and to explore the waters west of Olive Beadle. We come upon a family of hippo, heads out of the water, bobbing about playfully. We keep our distance: they are not to be trifled with.

We speed up the sun's path on the water, shooting forward over the golden ripples. Gradually, the sun sinks towards the distant horizon. It flushes to a gorgeous red and positions itself perfectly between two purple hills. The Zambian side of the river is bathed in pink light. Dusk is falling when we return to our mooring point.

In a few moments a million stars will light the African sky.

South African Airways Flight SA 0337 is now closed. We wish all passengers travelling on this flight a pleasant journey. We thank you for choosing to fly South African Airways and hope that you will be flying with us again soon.